AMERICAN LITTORAL SOCIETY
HANDBOOK FOR THE
MARINE NATURALIST

AMERICAN LITTORAL SOCIETY
HANDBOOK FOR THE
MARINE NATURALIST

DAVID K. BULLOCH

ILLUSTRATIONS BY
HELEN AND LOU BURLINGAME

Walker and Company
New York

First published in the United States of America in 1991 by Walker Publishing Company, Inc.

Published simultaneously in Canada by Thomas Allen & Son Canada, Limited, Markham, Ontario

Library of Congress Cataloging-in-Publication Data
Bulloch, David K.
    American Littoral Society handbook for the marine naturalist / by David K. Bulloch; illustrations by Helen and Lou Burlingame.
        p.   cm.
    Includes bibliographical references and index.
    ISBN 0-8027-1165-0 (cl). —ISBN 0-8027-7353-2 (pa)
    1. Marine biology.   I. Title.   II. Title: Handbook for the marine naturalist.
QH91.B775   1991
574.92—dc20   91-11538
                                                                  CIP

Printed in the United States of America

10 9 8 7 6 5 4 3 2 1

To Graham MacMillan, who founded and developed the American Littoral Society fish-tagging program and was a steadying influence in the society's formative days.

CONTENTS

ACKNOWLEDGMENTS

My thanks to Derek Bennett, executive director of the American Littoral Society for supporting the expansion of what initially was to have been a pamphlet into a full-fledged book, and for permission to reprint parts of articles that first appeared in the Society's publication, *Underwater Naturalist*.

I also appreciate the help of C.D. Hardy of Southhampton College whose marine ecology courses made use of many of the techniques described.

Tony Pacheco of the National Marine Fisheries Service (NMFS) was especially helpful in parts dealing with fish. Claire Steimle and Judy Berrien of the NMFS library at Sandy Hook, New Jersey aided me on numerous occasions.

Helen and Lou Burlingame did the illustrations and provided many helpful ideas.

And, of course, my wife, Edith, kept our lives on an even keel during the usual storms that surround a project of this sort.

PREFACE

The marine naturalist, along the shore or at sea, derives a great deal of pleasure from just looking. Purposeless observation, far from an idle waste of time, plants the seeds of curiosity and helps develop a quick and questioning eye.

It may also lead to pondering on what you see and a craving to know more about the place and its inhabitants.

If you decide to study your surroundings more thoroughly, you may find it helpful to become more organized about it. You may need repeated observations over one or several seasons to discover a trend, verify an idea, or come up with a new view on what you have seen. You may need a few measurements, either in the field or later at home, to round out your study.

But that is science, you say, and you are not a full-fledged, dyed-in-the-wool, certified scientist. Perhaps not, but science does not require a certificate or a license to practice. It requires an open, curious mind backed up by a reasonable willingness to expend some mental and physical effort.

Some of the methods of science lie well beyond the amateur naturalist's means and training, but the principles of science are available to all who pay heed to them. Coupled with simple methods and apparatus, you can apply them to an enormous range of investigations.

The purpose of this book is to supply you with a point from which to start or expand your own explorations. It contains suggestions on how to go about seeking answers, how to make those measurements that are relatively easy to do and worth doing using simple apparatus, and how to expand your first-hand knowledge of the marine world. It is far from all-inclusive; much is left up to you to chase further.

You are unlikely to make immediate use of every topic covered here, but the sea and its shores generate broad interests, so browse around in it and let it take you where it will. You may find yourself going down a new road. It may wind in unexpected ways and cross odd avenues you did not intend to visit, but the trip may grant you one of life's greatest pleasures—finding out for yourself.

American Littoral Society
Handbook for the Marine Naturalist

1

INQUIRY

You need no high-minded justification to go afield to the water; to walk the fringes of the marsh, the tidal flats of the bay, or the edge of a rocky shoreline. Perhaps you simply want the opportunity to relax and watch the waves, see what has washed up in the wrack with the last high tide, or wander the back dunes looking at birds or wildflowers.

Once there, your surroundings may soon unsettle your idle intentions and fill you with a sense of the delights and mysteries of this place where the land meets the sea. A scuttling crab, small fish darting in the shallows, odd mounds in the exposed mud flat, incrustations on rocks and wrack will all arouse your sense of curiosity.

You will find as many or more intriguing mysteries at sea. A school of mackerel flashing by near the surface, a whale breaching, or a dark patch on the water that turns out to be a green turtle sunning itself— almost every trip to sea will turn up something unexpected.

If you return time after time, mindless looking will not suffice; you will have too many questions needing answers. To satisfy your curiosity, you will fill your knapsack to overflowing with field guides. You will observe, take pictures, use your guides.

As time goes on, your questions will go beyond mere identification. What does this creature eat? With whom does it associate? Why does it live here and not somewhere else? You make notes. You make comparisons. You begin to read more about the niches in the ecosystem you see before you. Your curiosity develops a focus. You narrow your inquiry to a few specific subjects. You ponder, trying to make sense of the patterns that are beginning to emerge from what you have seen and thought about.

You are on the threshold of exploration. If you have not been down this road before, you will need a few words of guidance and access to a few useful tools. What follows is a mix of both. It is up to you to sort out what will serve you best.

This book will not make a marine scientist out of you. That takes years of formal education followed by direct field experience on a day-to-day basis. There is, however, nothing to stop you from becoming a competent marine naturalist. In many ways, for a given place and a given species, you can become every bit aware as to their ways and whereabouts as the specialist.

SEEING

Yogi Berra once remarked that "You can see a lot just by lookin'." In other words, pay attention to what you are looking at, and know what you are looking for. So much can go on so quickly, that as you look, you have to visually separate the wheat from the chaff. Your brain receives too much information to retain it all so you must put your mind to work in a hurry on what may be important and what can be quickly forgotten.

If you look at a fish and plan to identify it later, a lot more has to register than "It's fish-like." You must make mental notes of its colors, size, the general shape of its body, the number and kinds of dorsal fins, and the shape and size of its pectoral fins and tailfin. Even then, you may not have enough information to identify what species it is. You probably will have gleaned enough to determine that it is one of several choices and you will find out what distinguishing features will separate out those choices the next time you encounter it.

Spotting important differences from scratch (shape, color, markings, behavior) can be very difficult when you are on unfamiliar ground. Often you do not have much time to find distinguishing marks or tell-tale signs. You can shorten the learning process very simply. Associate with someone who is already at home in the territory and with the species you wish to explore. You can compress thousands of hours of observation into less than a hundred with the right person to guide you.

Nowhere is this more evident than in the tropics with its marvelous species diversity. Upon arrival, you are overwhelmed by the multitudes of fish, invertebrates, birds, plants, trees, and insects. Yet within weeks, given the company of a knowing mentor, you can learn to recognize hundreds of species. For example, it is possible to learn a hundred species of birds within a week with relative ease by the grace of association with a sharp-eyed naturalist who has visited there many times before.

Not all locales are equally easy to study. Tropical reef fish are so colorful and bizarre that you can learn the common ones quite quickly. In more temperate waters, many species have similar shapes and are uniformly brown or gray. In murky water, identification becomes a great deal more problematical.

One way to train yourself to pick up detail, especially if animal behavior interests you, is to keep an aquarium stocked with fish that have well-known and complicated lifestyles. The three-spined stickleback or a breeding pair of bettas have had volumes written about them. Watch them and compare what you see with what you read.

WRITE IT UP

If you take no other advice from this book, please take this: keep a journal. You may pride yourself upon having the memory of an elephant, but recall that elephants are not widely known for literate contributions to knowledge. Aside from that, your log or journal will measure much more than your interest in natural history; it cannot but reflect its keeper and changes in attitude and interests as the years pass.

Keeping a field diary is a critical part of field discovery. Perhaps it will be a chore at first, but in time it will become a well-found habit. It may not read too well in the beginning, but never mind. Simply learn from those early efforts and soon you will be producing readable prose.

What to record? Describe the events of the day, the surroundings, and prevailing conditions. Note the date and location. Assume that whoever reads your notes knows nothing about the place you have visited and you must bring it to life for them. Describe it, sketch it, take photos to include in the logbook later; in short, visualize it for the reader. If you go back to the same location time and again, build on earlier descriptions and refer the reader to your earlier writings.

Note the weather, temperature, state of the tide, and whatever else might affect what you have seen. Is fall early? Is this the first sunny day after two weeks of cold, rainy days? A calendar date only approximates

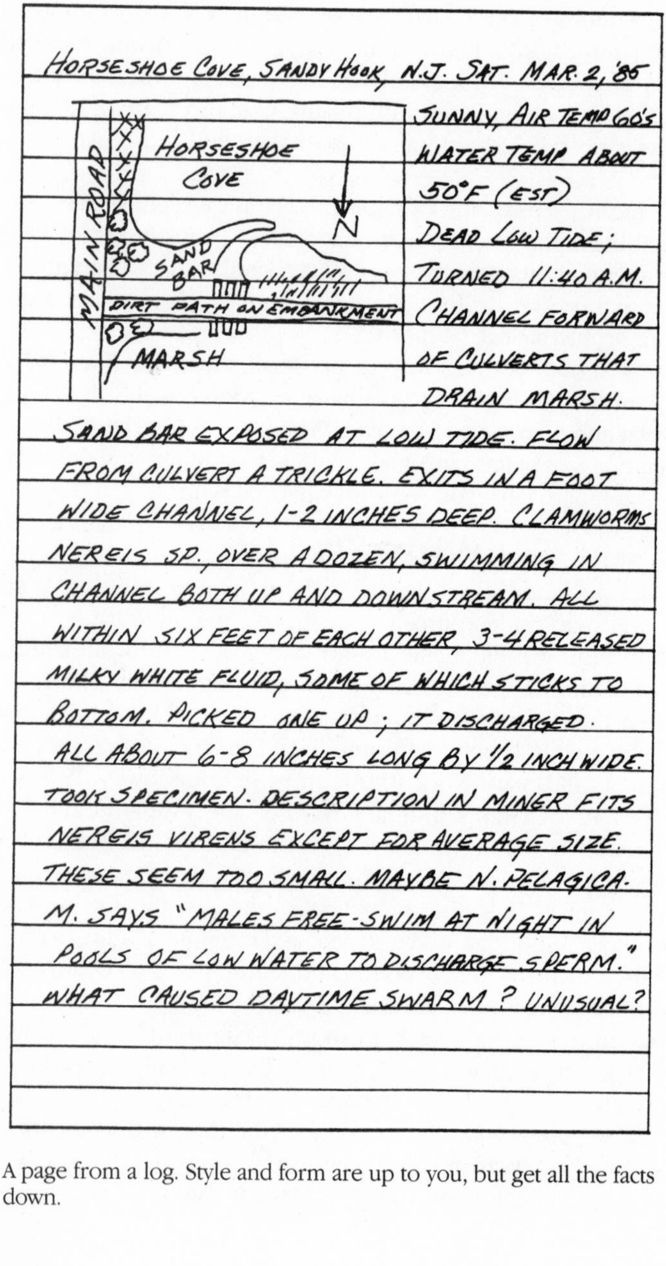

HORSESHOE COVE, SANDY HOOK, N.J. SAT. MAR. 2, '85

HORSESHOE COVE

MAIN ROAD

SAND BAR

DIRT PATH ON EMBANKMENT

MARSH

N

SUNNY, AIR TEMP 60's WATER TEMP ABOUT 50°F (EST) DEAD LOW TIDE; TURNED 11:40 A.M. CHANNEL FORWARD OF CULVERTS THAT DRAIN MARSH.

SAND BAR EXPOSED AT LOW TIDE. FLOW FROM CULVERT A TRICKLE. EXITS IN A FOOT WIDE CHANNEL, 1-2 INCHES DEEP. CLAMWORMS NEREIS SP. OVER A DOZEN, SWIMMING IN CHANNEL BOTH UP AND DOWNSTREAM. ALL WITHIN SIX FEET OF EACH OTHER, 3-4 RELEASED MILKY WHITE FLUID, SOME OF WHICH STICKS TO BOTTOM. PICKED ONE UP; IT DISCHARGED. ALL ABOUT 6-8 INCHES LONG BY ½ INCH WIDE. TOOK SPECIMEN. DESCRIPTION IN MINER FITS NEREIS VIRENS EXCEPT FOR AVERAGE SIZE. THESE SEEM TOO SMALL. MAYBE N. PELAGICA. M. SAYS "MALES FREE-SWIM AT NIGHT IN POOLS OF LOW WATER TO DISCHARGE SPERM." WHAT CAUSED DAYTIME SWARM? UNUSUAL?

A page from a log. Style and form are up to you, but get all the facts down.

4

what things are like in a given year and some background on what it has been like since your last entry can help give the reader a clearer picture of the scene.

Note the characters and events; who, what, where, how many, how long, how often, distances, directions, patterns. You may think much of this will be irrelevant, but write as though it will be different the next time you return. If there is too much to encompass by pen, use your camera. For example, the Fish and Wildlife Service conducts censuses of seal rookeries by simply taking aerial photos of breeding beaches every year at the same time. Most of the time this kind of data shows little of interest, but in the last five years certain rookeries in the Alaskan Straits have collapsed. The photos provide incontrovertible evidence to skeptics and believers alike.

Make note of references. Create cross-references to photos, sketches, recordings, video material, and collected samples so that you can review loose pieces of evidence in the future. You need not create too elaborate a system, but don't trust to memory; it will invariably fail you.

As you garner more and more material about a specific topic of interest—some of it personally uncovered by you and some gathered from the literature—occasionally summarize your findings in your journal. Writing it up often points up holes in your knowledge or flaws in your ideas which you can then correct.

You can organize your journal in any fashion you see fit. You might choose to write up your findings topic by topic, intertwining what you previously said about something with what you have recently seen that verifies or challenges your previous conclusions. You might choose to keep it chronologically, which is simpler but will result in a mix of topics.

Don't be afraid to pose questions and speculate on answers. Include commentary on what remains for you to find out and how you might go about it. Also include what others have said (but don't take it as gospel). Never fear that you are writing too much—you cannot write enough. When you look back on what you have written years hence, about half-forgotten expeditions, trips, and explorations, you will invariably regret that you did not write more about it and more often.

QUESTIONS AND ANSWERS

The heart of inquiry is the properly framed question. First, it must be answerable within the limits of your resources, you can allot only so much time, money, equipment, and training to it. Second, you should have a sensible reason for asking the question. Sheer curiosity is a very good reason.

Neither the question nor the answer need fulfill a grand purpose. Leave the value of the answer for others to judge. Time has a way of altering the measure of things, often unpredictably. Your answer may simply be "This is the way it is at this place at this time" which may not seem too significant now, but may be important at a future time.

For example, rapid population growth on the lands adjacent to our marine coastlines, our on-going release of toxic chemicals and huge quantities of wastes laden with nitrogen and phosphorus into our rivers, estuaries, and embayments, seriously threatens the life within these waters, reducing both diversity and numbers. As often as not, no one has surveyed many of these areas and we have no mileposts by which to assess the direct damage. This degradation can be slow as with seepage or sudden as with an oil spill. Either way, measures of what it was like before befouling began can be of considerable help in measuring its restoration.

Your questions can arise either from observation or by abstraction. You will likely pose most of them initially from what you have observed. Before pressing on, be sure to ask yourself "How valid are my observations?" Not that you should doubt your senses, for they are your main sources of information, but what you think you have observed must occur reasonably frequently, be reasonably reproducible, and be self-evident. You may see what others do not initially see, but if they fail to see it after you have pointed it out, you either have caught the thread of a deeper mystery or you have an unresolved cognition problem.

Constraints of time and resources will limit the breadth of your investigations, which must be narrow enough to be doable but not so confined or slanted as to pigeonhole an answer into a self-fulfilling prophecy.

Also keep in mind that answering questions that have already been asked and answered before is far from a fruitless enterprise. Not only does it help train you in the methods that scientists employ, but often leads to unexpected finds. The conditions under which you observe the object of your investigation will almost never be the same as those of an earlier investigator and you may uncover an inexplicable difference in results. You can then happily plunge into the three main possibilities these results infer; you may be wrong, the previous investigator may have been wrong, or the animal or its surroundings may have changed in some unknown fashion that has altered the results.

PROBLEM SOLVING

Answering a question and solving a problem are semantic cousins, often indistinguishable from each other. The art of doing either from evidence is what scientific inquiry is all about. The problem is often the evidence. What constitutes sound evidence is not as straightforward as you may initially envision, but more on this shortly.

The route to the solution of a problem is cloudier than most practicing scientists care to admit. The final product of a scientist, a published paper, may be a paragon of clarity and order, but the path to its conclusions often evolve by a murky and chaotic process. Few scientists ever let on to the dead ends, false starts, botched experiments, muddled reasoning, and faulty premises that litter the trail of many an investigation that finally reaches a successful conclusion.

As untidy as the path to an answer may be, it tends to resolve itself into distinct segments. The hardest part, most scientists agree, is the first—the awareness that a problem worth answering lies within your means to do it. You may ask "Who lives here?" or "How does this animal's behavior aid in its survival?" which seem simple enough, but which may turn out to be too broad, too complex, or too elusive to answer.

As you proceed and collect data, tentative answers and explanations will come and go. Conjectures and half-truths will fall as evidence mounts. Don't despair; this is all part of the process. What finally will emerge is a working hypothesis.

HYPOTHESIS

The formation and testing of a hypothesis is the foundation of the scientific method. Your objective is to design your inquiry in such a way as to attack the cornerstone upon which the hypothesis rests. If your evidence leaves that structure intact, the hypothesis *may* be true. If the hypothesis is contradicted, then it is time to formulate a new one.

If your question cannot be tested, then it is not answerable by science. "What is the meaning of life?" is a classic example of an often-asked question. The scientist will tell you the answer may lie in the province of the theologian or the philosopher, but being a query that isn't amenable to testing, science cannot directly help answer it.

Scientific "truth" does not come easily, and what now exists leads a tentative existence. The concepts we embrace today, the current paradigms as they are called, may not hold up over time. Much is demanded of them. Not only must they withstand repeated assault, they must predict new and unforeseen relationships. For "truth" to remain intact, it must constantly survive challenge and continually prove useful.

A caveat here—the design of a study is often laid out with a preconceived notion about its outcome and inadvertently skewed to prove an unwarranted assumption. It is one thing to create a working hypothesis and set up a test of its validity. It is quite another to pick and choose among the approaches looking only for supporting evidence to reach a foregone conclusion. The latter course is not scientific inquiry; it is polemic or sophistry.

The temptation to slant the argument is especially strong these days in the realm of environmental issues. We are all aware of environmental damage, but to overexaggerate a particular incident or condition (or understate it, for that matter) is to do a disservice to those who may have to set priorities for the expenditure of time and money to remediate it.

EXPERIMENTS

When you think about how to test a hypothesis, you may have a choice between using the natural environment as your laboratory or a more controlled setting. Scientists tend to pick the latter; it is more convenient, consistent, reproducible (or so they like to think), and measurements are easier to make. For life below a certain size or a certain organizational level, using the lab may be essential. The higher up the scale of complexity, the more its ways are inextricably woven into its milieu and the more likely field work is essential. This is especially true in the study of behavior. However, more and more evidence points to the same being true, at least in part, for lower animals, primarily because the lab rarely replicates the outdoors in every respect.

"Controlled laboratory conditions" cancel out an unknown number of stimuli that otherwise would surely impinge from moment to moment on a captive animal which may be indispensible to its well-being, or at the least, to its normal "world view"; in short, a dull environment can quickly produce a creature with dulled senses and little of the spontaneity needed for its survival in the wild.

Current thought among scientists leans toward quantification over description. The argument goes: If your methods are valid, they can be confirmed by others who will generate like numbers, and if confirmed, future change is much easier to spot if using a numerical format rather than a descriptive one.

This view has not gone unchallenged among scientists. Konrad Lorenz, a co-founder of ethology, was especially critical of the drift toward quantification. He felt that although experimentation at the expense of observation may create no methodological error, it forces the scientist to concentrate on those aspects of behavior which readily lend themselves to experimentation which leads to "explanatory monism"; that is, a far narrower view of the animal's total capabilities.

Gathering numbers has its own problems. Choosing the samples from which the numbers will be generated can be critical. Once the samples have been chosen and the measurements made, what to make of the numbers (and the samples) is not always straightforward. Some cause-effect relationships are relatively unequivocal; ballpark numbers will spell out a definitive connection. But if the effect is small or the measurement error large, you will have to deal with the numbers in a special way.

NUMBERS

Whether you are about to collect your own numbers or are looking at numbers generated by others, you should know something about the problems of getting them and interpreting them when they are taken from the real world. Just as the wise carpenter heeds the maxim "measure twice and cut once" so, too, you must be aware of the pitfalls in gathering and using them.

Generally numbers are gotten by measuring a group of like things and are used to compare them with another set of measurements of like things that differ, as far as you can tell, only in that aspect you wish to compare. For example, are the mud snails living over here doing as well, as judged by body weight, as the mud snails living over there, where the bottom sediments contain less organic matter? To be comparable, the same numbers of snails must be randomly collected at both locales (you can get away with sample size differences but it complicates computations later on), and weighed in a consistent manner; that is, the numbers must be collected under like circumstances and the measurements made by a consistent method.

Measured numbers taken from a set of similar things show two characteristics: central tendency and variation. Those similar things make up part of what the mathematician calls a universe or population. Don't get the mathematical definition confused with the biological one—the concept of population to the mathematician is simply an abstraction that separates the sample from a universe of conceptually like things. All you can glean about that abstract population will have to be inferred from the sample you have drawn.

Your measurements on those samples you have drawn have two sources of error: their own natural variation and measurement error. (You may have also made methodological errors as well; for example in the snail experiment you may have mixed in different species or chosen specimens that had not reached maturity as yet.) Natural variation tends to be random and is therefore distributed according to the laws of probability. Measurement errors, usually much smaller in magnitude than natural variation, can be both random and biased; that is, in addition to measurement variations, the device you use may have a constant error built in to it. Normally you will discover and correct for this by calibrating your measuring device.

As variation increases, the size of the sample must increase so that random errors will tend to cancel out, thus making averages more reliable. With too few samples, results may be skewed by random variation; with too many, you may find the experiment becoming too large to handle.

Your measurements will cluster around some average value. Almost without exception, you will use the arithmetic average, but in some instances, other averages such as the mode or the median may serve you better. (See a statistics text to find out more about them and when they are applicable.)

If you decide to ask yourself whether the measurements from two groups of things suggest they are alike or different, you hope the differences between the two groups are great enough to clearly distinguish them apart, or so close as to render them comfortably indistinguishable.

Too often the differences will fall into a gray area where the distinctions between the two sets of numbers is not clear. This uncertainty is exacerbated by large, random variation which clouds the issue of whether or not a real difference exists. Where do you draw the line? At what point do the averages between the two sets of numbers become significant, or can you regard them all as from the same (mathematical) population? If your question hinges on the significance of the difference, you must have an available method that tells you the probability that you are dealing with two universes or one. Such is the task of statistics.

AVERAGES AND VARIATION

The most common measure of the central tendency of a set of numbers is the arithmetic average or arithmetic mean or simply the mean, as it is often called. Just add up the measurements and divide by the number of samples measured.

Variation from the arithmetic mean may be expressed several ways. The range, the absolute difference between the highest and lowest of the values you averaged, is simple to find but of limited use. More difficult to calculate but more analytically powerful, is the standard deviation, a measure of the dispersion of the data which is related to the normal probability distribution of random occurrences. The standard deviation is so derived that plus or minus one standard deviation unit will encompass 68% of the data; two units, 95%; and three units, 99.7%.

Statistical techniques are available that will provide you with a rational way to compare sample averages and show you the degree of risk to take in making a claim of sameness or difference. Statistical methods also provide ways to lay out an experimental design such that differences introduced by the test method can be separated from inherent differences that you seek to show or disprove.

Don't be dismayed by the strange notations you will uncover when you first open a statistics text. Almost all the procedures involve nothing more difficult than adding, subtracting, multiplying, dividing, squaring numbers, and deriving square roots. This does not mean, however, that you can blindly crank out statistics without knowing the principles upon which they are based. The fundamentals of probability are critical concepts to both the generator of statistics and to those who would interpret their results. There is plenty of room for error, and mathematically based misjudgments occur because either the initiator or the user did not correctly apply the theory of probability.

CORRELATION

If you are seeking a cause-and-effect relationship, you will anticipate that some measured input will evoke a mathematically predictable response. That relationship might be linear (one to one, for example) or more complex.

The simplest way to detect the possibility of a correlation between two sets of corresponding numbers is to plot the data pairs on a simple X-Y chart. If a strong correlation exists, a telltale predictive pattern will emerge. For example, all the points may fall on a straight line, suggesting a strong linear relationship. Conversely, if no relationship exists, your plot will look like a shotgun pattern; that is, the points will appear randomly scattered.

Because a mathematical correlation exists does not necessarily mean there is a significant connection between the two sets of observations. Two sets of numbers can trend in the same direction for reasons that have nothing to do with each other. As an example, consider the height of two growing seedlings of different species. Over a certain period of their growth they are bound to show a positive correlation, but that correlation is a reflection of the sunshine, moisture, and nutrients they received (as well as the fact that they are both young plants) and not due to an interrelationship between them.

You may never set up a statistically designed test and yet still have a need to know the fundamental principles involved. The main reason will be that you may find yourself reading the work of scientists who may or may not have used these methods. It can be quite surprising to delve into the data given in a scientific paper and find yourself at odds with (or at least in doubt about) its conclusions. You may be mistaken in your assessment, but it's a sure sign that you are thinking.

THE METRIC SYSTEM

Scientists invariably report their results in mks units; that is, they measure length, weight, and time in increments of the meter, kilogram, and second. In addition, volume is measured in liters and temperature measured in degrees Celsius, whose scale is based on the freezing point of water (0°C) and its boiling point (100°C).

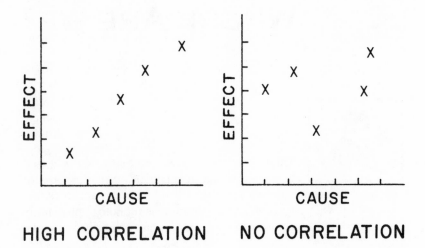

HIGH CORRELATION   **NO CORRELATION**

If the points in the graph fall along a line or curve, either rising or falling steadily, there is strong correlation between cause and effect; if scattered, little or none.

The English system, an odd mix of weight scales (avoirdupois, troy, and apothecaries), measures (U.S. liquid and dry, British imperial liquid and dry) as well as distances in inches, feet, yards, and miles was to have been phased out of the United States by 1992 to meet a growing demand for international standardization, but it persists; we still buy our lumber in feet, our potatoes in pounds, and our gasoline in gallons.

If you do not have a feel for metric units, develop one. It is especially valuable in short measurements. You need only remember a few conversions: an inch is 25.4 millimeters, a meter is just over 39 inches (a little more than a yard), a quart is nearly a liter (946 ml), a pleasant 68°F day is 20°C and body temperature, 98.6°F is 37°C.

You will find a mixture of systems in this book. No sense sending you to the hardware store looking for 13 mm galvanized mesh when ½-in. is the conventional measure. You will also find measures appropriate to the subject: Ship's speed is given in knots (one knot equals 1.2 statute miles per hour).

2

WHERE ARE WE?

Whether you choose to explore a rocky shore, a sand beach, a tidal marsh, a bay, or offshore, sooner or later you will come upon a place to which you will want to return. Perhaps you will want to conduct an experiment, rephotograph a shoreline shifted by a storm, resurvey the marine life, or just have another look.

You can trust your memory or luck to find your way back, but don't count on either. Shifting sand or a recollection faded over time may conspire to fool you and leave you wishing you had made a few notes and a sketch or two before your first departure. The notes themselves will remind you that you want to revisit the place and why.

If your travels take you far afield or asea, correlating notes, maps, charts, and photos at home becomes even more essential. That trip to the Outer Banks in North Carolina will provide its share of scenic views. A return visit after a major storm has passed through may alter former features and render them barely recognizable. Your notebook and attached photos will tell you just how much has changed and in what way.

Shoreline shifts are fascinating to follow. Your favorite beach may appear immutable, but a single northeaster (or northwester if you live on the Pacific Coast) can move an astonishing amount of sand and leave the place considerably altered. And with a hurricane even greater changes take place: new inlets appear; trees disappear; docks and houses vanish—in short, total rearrangement.

Not only will the physical landscape above and below water be altered, but the endemic flora and fauna may also be seriously affected.

Recall that the kinds of sea grasses, seaside plants, and shrubs that grow in a particular location reflect the kind of soil, moisture, salinity, and nutrients they receive. A storm may sweep away sediments, a new inlet cut by the waters will likely increase the salinity and change the circulation patterns of the bay it enters, a salt marsh may be unexpectedly flooded with a deluge of rainwater and lose many of its salt-loving animals and plants. Even rainfall patterns can affect who lives where. A typical example is the range of the oyster drill in major oyster-bearing estuaries which is directly related to the average salinity of its bottom water. A few dry seasons can so diminish the flow of a river that the drill will invade much farther upstream than in normal seasons.

Changes may come on gradually. A beach may be building up or washing away, but it may take several seasons before the process becomes evident. Not only will a beach change because of alongshore littoral drift, but its profile will change seasonally; that is, from a period of calm seas which will slowly build up the shoreline to a period of stormy seas during which the waves will carve out the lower beach within a few cycles of the tide.

Comparing "before" and "after" sketches and photographs may point up the ephemeral nature of the coastline. They will also vividly point up problems caused by excessive shoreline development and its consequences. The encroachment of civilization, no matter how benign, almost always has deleterious effects. As an example, get a map of those areas in your state where shellfishing is prohibited and overlay it on a state map showing population density. Invariably the two will show a close correlation.

Just keep in mind, if you really want to get "before" and "after" scenarios, you have to get the "befores" now. When you take those photographs be sure to provide yourself with enough information to know where you were when you took them so that repeat photos may be taken from the same place years hence. Make notes on exactly where you were standing, in what compass direction you pointed the camera. Remember, if you use a manmade feature as a guidepost in the picture, it may not be there when you return! Also note the focal length of the lens with which you took the picture. This will give you or the viewer of your photo an idea of the angle of view that the photo encompasses and remind you of what to use when you retake the scene.

Local photos, well documented, are surprisingly rare considering the billions of pictures that have been taken since George Eastman made both camera and film so easily accessible. Most photos have long been discarded, or their present owners have no idea of what they are looking at, when the picture was taken, or where it was taken from.

DETERMINING YOUR POSITION

Whether you intend to explore alongshore or at sea, begin by getting either a map of the area or a nautical chart. Two main types will prove useful. Topographic maps published by the Geological Survey of the Department of the Interior cover United States land areas. Nautical charts provided by the National Ocean Service of NOAA cover the U.S. shorelines. You can deal directly with the federal government for topos or go to a local sporting goods store that specializes in hiking. For charts try your local marine supply dealer.

If you do not already understand the symbols and notations on a nautical chart, either browse through the latest edition of Chapman's *Piloting, Seamanship, and Small Boat Handling* or write to the National Ocean Survey, Rockville, Maryland 20852 for the latest edition of the Nautical Chart Manual, Chart No. 1: Nautical Chart Symbols and Abbreviations. Also ask them for the Nautical Chart catalog for the region of interest to you; No. 1: Atlantic and Gulf Coasts (which includes Puerto Rico and the Virgin Islands), No. 2: Pacific Coast (including Hawaii and other U.S. Pacific island possessions), No. 3: Alaska (including the Aleutian Islands) or No. 4: Great Lakes and Adjacent Waterways.

You will find these maps and charts cover a great deal of territory at too small a scale for your purposes. Nautical charts rarely have a scale interval of less than 1:40,000 (one inch on the chart is equivalent to 3,300 feet) with the exception of a few harbor charts. Geological Survey quadrangle maps (topos), the 7.5 minute series, have a scale interval of 1:24,000 (one inch equals 2,000 feet).

To get a chart of a small area, you will have to sketch one for yourself. To get started you might begin with a tracing from a county map, an aerial survey map, or a do-it-yourself enlargement from whatever you can find that represents that area. You can blow up the portion you need by using an enlarging copying machine or sketch an enlargement using a grid system. Using grids rather than doing it freehand will increase the accuracy of your transfer.

Lay a sheet of translucent onion skin engineering graph paper that

ENLARGING
A CHART

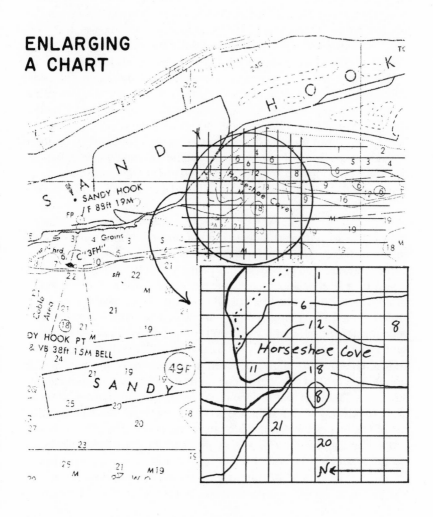

This simple enlargement method allows you to eliminate unnecessary
details and add pertinent ones at the scene.

contains small square divisions over the area of the chart that you intend to enlarge. On another sheet of paper lay out a grid of larger squares, whose size you will determine by the degree of enlargement you require. Transfer the information from each small square on the original to the appropriate "enlarged" square on your sketch. If you can, include landmarks that may be useful for triangulation. Also include scale, compass directions, and a latitude-longitude line.

If you are charting a shoreline where the tides make a considerable difference to what fraction of the shoreline is exposed you must decide whether you will choose to use the conventional "mean low water" datum or visit the site during a new moon or full moon low water when the "spring" tides prevail. This will reveal the full (or nearly so) extent of land exposure. A few photographs of some prominent landmark near the water line during a spring low and a spring high tide will also help you gauge the extent of the effects of the tidal cycle.

LAND POSITION

If you plan to return to a specific location time and again to follow seasonal changes on a small patch of shallow, submerged bottom or a more landward patch, you should plan to establish some permanent points of reference and where your patch is relative to them; a recognizable rock, piling, abutment or other nearby fixture will do.

If nothing of a "permanent" nature is nearby, choose several well recognizable stable, landward references farther away—a house, a standpipe, a cupola, tower, or the like will do. From where you wish to return, measure the angles between at least three of these reference points. You can do this with a commercial transit or a homemade instrument. Simply mount a 0-360° protractor on a piece of ¾" plywood and provide a swiveling sight line whose center coincides with the center of the protractor. On the bottom of the board affix a ¼-20 teenut adapter so that the unit can be mounted on a tripod. A bubble level set on the board will be useful to set up the unit on a horizontal plane. Because you can only measure angles to the nearest degree, your unit will not be as precise as a commercial transit (but it won't be nearly as expensive, either).

By referring to these angles at a future time, you will be able to re-establish your original position within a few feet. If your reference points appear on a nautical chart, you can transfer the angles to the

HOMEMADE TRANSIT

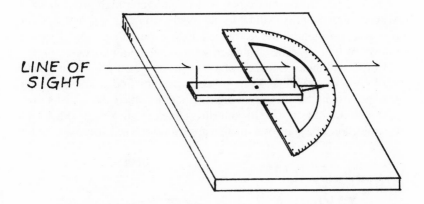

LINE OF SIGHT

Find the angle between two bearings by aligning them sequentially along the swiveling arm. (Note that the swivel arm has been deliberately shortened to show the pointer from which the bearing angles are read.)

chart and pinpoint your position on it. This is similar to charting a position over water which we will discuss next.

SEA POSITION

Finding your exact position at sea is a different matter from finding your way at sea. Inshore piloting and offshore navigation serve two needs; to find out approximately where you are and to determine what direction to follow to get to where you want to go. Neither requires pinpoint accuracy.

Piloting and offshore navigation are essential skills to the seafarer. The U.S. Power Squadron teaches both elementary and advanced courses in piloting and navigation. If you plan to skipper your own boat, you should consider taking their courses as well as safety courses taught by the U.S. Coast Guard Auxiliary. Also helpful is *Chapman Piloting,*

Seamanship, and Small Boat Handling referred to earlier and available in most marine supply stores.

If you intend to transfer information gathered at sea to a chart or you intend to return to the same position at another time, positional accuracy becomes paramount. Inshore in bays, river mouths, and estuaries, or along the seacoast, you can make good use of clearly identifiable objects such as tanks, standpipes, towers, and other high promontories. Many of these features will be found plotted on nautical charts. You can plot your position by the horizontal angle method mentioned earlier, but you will need somewhat more sophisticated equipment.

Horizontal angles between objects can be measured with a sextant held sideways or with an Ilon or Weems position finder. These devices, like the sextant, have a mirror arrangement in which you adjust a pivot arm until two objects, one in your direct line of sight and the other seen by reflection in the pivotal mirror, are superimposed over each other.

TAKING A BEARING ANGLE

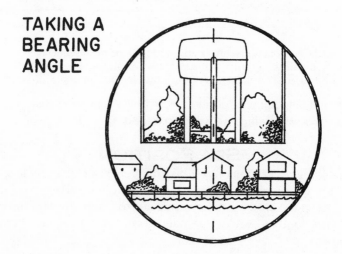

Find the angle between two shore bearings by aligning the direct view (*below*) with the one seen in the sextant mirror (*above*).

The pivot arm is calibrated in degrees and fractions of a degree and the angle between the two objects can be read directly.

Read two horizontal angles between three objects; that is, determine the angle between the left-hand object and the middle object and the angle between the middle object and the right-hand object.

To transfer that position to a chart, set the angles on a three-arm protractor, a plotting device especially designed for the two-horizontal-angles method, or using an ordinary protractor, draw the angles on a piece of translucent paper. Align either the three-arm protractor or the translucent paper on the chart such that all three objects fall on the lines; that is, the arms of the protractor or lines on the paper should simultaneously intersect the objects. Your position lies at the intersection of the three lines. To avoid ambiguity, try to pick objects that fall in nearly a straight line, and if possible, such that the middle object is closest to the observer. If that is not possible, develop an additional line of position. A compass bearing will do. Don't use it in plotting; use it as a double check to avoid reversing the bearing inadvertently.

Although inshore navigation is done by compass bearings, do not use them to plot accurate positions. Accurate compass readings are easier said than done even in a flat, calm sea with the compass well corrected for deviation. A small boat turns under you quickly and bearings will have large enough errors to make the return trip difficult.

To get back to the original position, proceed to the general locale and set the angle of one of the pair of bearings on the sextant or finder. (You can obtain an inexpensive, plastic sextant in a marine supply store as well as a position finder and a three-arm protractor.) If the angle between the objects is too wide, go further offshore on a course that is on the midline between the two objects; if too narrow, proceed inshore. All the positions that have the same angle between two objects will fall on the arc of a circle. Visualize that arc, then proceed along it until the other bearing is duplicated. With a little practice you can return to the same position time and again with uncanny precision.

Along a coastline that is heavily built up, another method works well. Once on the site, study the coastline for towers (for example, water towers, radio towers, transmission towers) that you can positively identify. As often as not, a house built along the coast will appear in line with it. With binoculars and notepad, sketch exactly how the tower and house line up and a description of the house as well as the ones next to it (the house you are using may get a paint job before you return). Take another bearing using another tower well up or down coast of the first set of bearings. When you return, match up one bearing, then proceed inshore or offshore until the other bearing lines up. Drop a marker buoy (a plastic bottle painted bright red tied to a sashweight; the line should be about ten feet longer than the local depth) and hunt in a circle around that with a recording depth finder or grapnel until you come across the wreck, shelf, or whatever is down there that you want to revisit.

The bearing method will do well for positions up to three to four miles offshore. You can occasionally get bearings as far away as eight miles, but don't expect to see them except on crisp, clear days and without considerable familiarity with the shoreline.

ELECTRONIC POSITION FINDING

For accurate positions at sea, LORAN C is the electronic system of choice for the small boatman on a limited budget. Portable receivers are now available for well under $1,000. Where transmission stations are positioned so that the lines of position broadcast from two stations approach 90° positional accuracy is close enough to return you to within fifty feet of the same spot well out of sight of land.

LORAN, LOng RAnge Navigation, is a hyperbolic system in which the difference in distance between two shore transmitters is found by measuring the arrival time difference between two pulse-modulated synchronized signals. These signals are produced by a "chain"—a master station and several slave stations. Chains are placed so that the lines of position they create are as close to right angles to each other as geographical placement will allow and cover the most heavily trafficked global air and sea lanes.

Although these transmissions are reliable, nothing is foolproof. Occasional breakdowns and, more often, electrical interference from thunderstorms, may upset signal reception. Obviously, if you're going far offshore, you should not rely on it as your sole means of navigation.

Modern LORAN C units present the data either as latitude-longitude lines or directly as lines of time differences. Many nautical charts now have LORAN lines overprinted on them. Because these lines are closer together than latitude-longitude lines, most users prefer to work with them.

LORAN C has found great favor among those who wish to return to the same position time and again to fish or carry on other activities. Divers revisiting wrecks simply go to the "numbers", drop a buoy, and verify their position with a depth finder. Similarly, offshore fishermen use it to relocate traps and nets.

3

WHAT IS IT?

Any casual outing to the coast or trip to sea will, during its course, bring you face to face with some unfamiliar thing. It may be plant or animal, seaweed or invertebrate, or it may appear so mysterious that you cannot place its kingdom.

Although much of the life in and near marine waters is unfamiliar, you already know something about it either from common knowledge or from what you have seen on televised nature programs or at a local aquarium.

Some creatures are easy enough to classify in a broad fashion, but more difficult to pin down to the exact species, either because they are not easy to see in their entirety, as with viewing whales from a boat; or their close relatives look so much alike, as with many sharks; or you simply do not get the opportunity to see them often enough to quickly distinguish among them.

When it comes to the invertebrates—animals without backbones— you plunge into a realm of hundreds of thousands of species (fortunately all do not co-exist in a single area), many small and cryptic, with forms, habits, and associations completely foreign to you.

Still, you recognize an anemone, a jellyfish, a crab, a shrimp, a lobster, a clam, a whelk, an octopus, a sea star (formerly called starfish). You can describe the differences between them and recognize the similarities between some of them; you know that all bivalves (two-shelled creatures like clams and scallops) are more alike than all gastropods (snail-like creatures) although both are mollusks and much different than sea stars, which are echinoderms. You probably know that the sea star is related to the sand dollar and the sea urchin, although you may have never laid eyes on another relative, the sea cucumber.

When it comes to worm-like critters, you may have used a clamworm for bait but did not know it is a polychaete or how it is related to other worm-like things you might have turned up while digging for clams or bait.

You know from your travels, even from those armchair travels in front of the television set, that most places contain many creatures that look similar to ones you know from home, but are obviously not of the same species. Some places you may have visited, the tropics especially, contain many more species than other places. For example, the tropics have many species of fish, but not many of each species, while in more temperate waters there are fewer species but many more of each.

ANIMALS

How then do you go about learning more about what is out there? Let's concentrate on animals. First, you need to know broadly how zoologists organize animal life. The main groups of animals in the animal kingdom are the phyla (the equivalent kind of groupings in plants are called divisions). Each phylum has a distinctly different structural plan from other phyla. Some phyla contain only a few species, some are rare and cryptic, and some are well known and contain hundreds of thousands of species.

In the hierarchy of the animal kingdom, phyla are subdivided into classes, classes into orders, orders into families, families into genera, and genera into species. Some species are subdivided into races, varieties, breeds, or whatever term might appropriately distinguish distinct members of a species. In large, complex phyla, such as Arthropoda, for example, further subdivisions like subphyla, subclasses, superorders, and so forth may be used to accommodate all the variation in shape, form, and function that nature has created and left the beleaguered biologist to cope with.

Almost all zoology texts organize their material by phyla into a similar manner; they start with those phyla assumed to be the least complex and proceed through to the most complex forms. Reclassification is an almost continuous affair and rearrangements of large groups are as common as reshuffling in small, obscure groups. This leads to inconsistencies among texts that can be disconcerting to the beginning reader.

Just remember the animals have had no hand in these doings; it's all a matter of what the current views among humans are on how they should be categorized.

Biologists now recognize five (or more) kingdoms: Monera, Protoctista (sometimes called Protista), Fungi, Plantae, and Animalia. Formerly it was just two, plants and animals, but jamming such diverse groups as viruses, bacteria, fungi, and unicellular organisms into one or the other simply refused to logically work, and those groups are now considered unique enough to deserve their own castles (viruses still present a dilemma and are accorded a different status nearly every time the list is rearranged). In the past, the unicellulars were with the animals—in the phylum Protozoa—and you will still see that arrangement in many fairly recent books.

If we drop extinct phyla, the rare ones, and the truly obscure, the phyla list for kingdom Animalia looks something like this.

Porifera—sponges
Cnidaria (formerly Coelenterata)—jellyfish, anemone, corals, sea
    fans, etc.
Ctenophora—comb jellies
Platyhelminthes—flatworms
Nemertea—proboscis worms
Aschelminthes—nematodes, rotifers, gastrotrichs, etc.
Chaetognatha—arrow-worms
Lophophora—bryozoa, brachiopoda, phoronida
Annelida—segmented worms
Mollusca—chitons, bivalves, gastropods, cephalopods
Arthropoda—a superphylum of shrimps, lobsters, crabs, isopods,
    copepods, spiders, mites, centipedes, insects, etc.
Echinodermata—sea lilies, sea stars, brittle stars, sea urchins, sea
    cucumbers and others.
Chordata—tunicates, lancets, vertebrates (including humans)

The vertebrates, although technically a sub-phylum, are usually singled out for separate treatment. They include fish, amphibians, reptiles, birds, and mammals.

To get a grip on lower animal life, the invertebrates, look over Buchbaum's *Animals Without Backbones* before hitting more complex texts.

The pictures and drawings will rapidly acquaint you with the shapes and forms of an enormous range of animals which will make the initial job of species identification a bit easier.

You can also get a better grasp of the phyla by referring to something a bit lighter at first. Many "beach stroller" books now abound for specific segments of coastline. If written by a biologist, they are sure to be organized by phyla and may offer you an easier initial bite into a big, unknown lump.

The United States coastline does not harbor the same species over its entire length. Geographic separation leads to different species, as does water temperature and a host of other factors. Along the east coast, the coast from Labrador to Cape Cod is distinct from Cape Cod to Cape Hatteras. Below Cape Hatteras the water remains relatively warm year-round and the species in it are more closely allied with those in the northern coast of the Gulf of Mexico. In southern Florida, the creatures in the Keys, for example, have a strong affinity with Caribbean critters.

Our Pacific coast does not undergo the seasonal temperature extremes of the Atlantic coast. Southern California water ranges from 54° to 74°F and contains species that are found well down the Baja Peninsula. The seasonal range from 46° to 64°F in central and northern California narrows into colder year-round temperatures northward into Washington, but is still not as extreme as winter temperatures off Maine.

What creatures live along any particular coastline depends on wave exposure, tidal exposure, and the kind of bottom. In quiet waters below the tides, salinity, temperature extremes, and bottom type do the sorting. Within each region there are a host of specific locales that have their own unique habitats. New England may be rocky, but sand beaches and tidemarshes are easy to find where rivers and streams come down to meet the sea. Some beaches in Maine are not made up of sand; that is, quartz, but consist almost entirely of shell and crushed carbonate remains of sea creatures. In Florida, beaches are mainly crushed shell or "sand" made of lime derived from corals and limey algae. In California, some beaches seasonally come and go; they are washed out, then rebuilt by the sea.

GUIDES AND MANUALS

When you turn to field guides and manuals to find out what is where and what it is, you will find that the animals may be arranged by differences in phyla, region, or habitat. Even if you restrict yourself to one region, you will find that a single guide is far from sufficient. You are apt to find guides that cover fish, water birds, seaside plants, shrubs and trees, tidepool animals, plankton, ecological relationships, and more for the specific region in which you live.

Many guides are strictly identification manuals. Their subject matter may be restricted to a single class, such as birds, or cover a broader spectrum like invertebrates. Those are arranged by phyla and describe each species mainly from an anatomical point of view even if only on a superficial level; that is, its basic outward appearance and not much about its inner construction or about how its inner works differ among its close or distant relatives. Now and then you will come across a manual that combines both the biology of the class, order, and family with individual species descriptions. Don't pass it by; over the years it will provide you with an easily accessible source of basic information about whatever species presently interests you without you having to plow through a great deal of specialized literature.

Other manuals contain only a few representative species and thoroughly discuss the anatomy and physiology of each. At some later date, when your appetite for a more fundamental grounding in biology has risen to a point where you are willing to exert some serious effort, you might give such a work a reasonable try. These kinds of volumes have usually been written as supplements to college courses so don't expect to breeze through them as you would a novel.

Still other guides concentrate on environments and ecological relationships within those environments, introducing each species in its turn as the author describes a particular locale or generalized habitat. Some authors expect the reader to not only know the animal but know it by its scientific name and may give no clue at all as to its general appearance. Most, however, realize that this approach, while it saves a great deal of space in which to cover other things, limits the usefulness of the book to specialists. Furthermore, not too many biologists have all the scientific names of the myriad creatures in their physical area of interest on the tip of their tongue.

Nevertheless, get used to the idea of the scientific name. Whether you are and intend to remain an amateur naturalist or plan to enter a career in the biological sciences, you will find, like the professional biologist, that the scientific name is the universal designation for each species. Its use eliminates ambiguity and the problem that different areas have different common names for the same creature.

For many creatures there is no common name. They are so cryptic or so poorly known by the populace, they have never been dubbed with an everyday appellation. On the other hand, the names of some common species have been given such terrible tongue-twisters that even the scientists have provided "official" common names for them. The American Fisheries Society provides a handbook of official common names and their scientific equivalents, upgrading and adding to it as usage changes, scientific names change, or new species pop up. However, the scientific literature often uses just the scientific name and not the common name; even if the common name is well entrenched and widely used; calling the quahog, for instance, *Mercenaria mercenaria,* or the blue crab, *Callinectes sapidus.*

Note that the scientific name consists of two parts; the first, the genus, is always capitalized and the second, the species, is never capitalized even if it is derived from a proper noun. You may occasionally see a third name which is varietal. For example, the Atlantic herring is called *Clupea harengus harengus* while the Pacific herring is called *Clupea harengus pallasi.* Both are so closely related that specialists hesitate to assign them to separate species but both are so geographically removed from each other and have different habits that scientists also hesitate to claim that they are exactly alike.

At the end of a scientific name you also may see a proper name and perhaps a year (in parentheses). That is the namer of the species and the year the creature was first described. Since the system was started by a Swedish botanist, Carolus Linnaeus, and he initially named the more common animals and plants, you may see the designation (L.) after a scientific name that he first described. If you want to find out more about this system, look up "binomial nomenclature" in a first year college biology textbook, or try an encyclopedia. The whole idea has been going strong since the late eighteenth century and nothing else has risen to challenge it.

Each guide emphasizes something different. A regional guide will escort you through an area's general morphology and major ecosystems, be they coral reefs, mangroves, and sand flats or barrier islands, estuaries, and rocky shores. It will then go into more detail on the communities within those ecosystems—salt marshes, mud flats, and

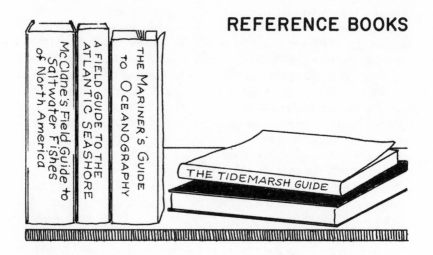

REFERENCE BOOKS

Collect as many reference books as you can afford for regions you regularly visit or would like to visit. Then read, read, read, visit, and read some more.

eelgrass beds within an estuary, for example—introducing you to the creatures that live there and their life-styles.

A regional guide may not say much about the characteristics that are helpful in identifying a plant or animal or how they are biologically related to one another. For that, you must turn to a manual whose purpose it is to denote the distinguishing features among closely related species within a given geographic region so that you can tell them apart.

Still other books, organized by habitat, emphasize the animals within specific zones, such as those living on wharf pilings, on upper tidal rocky shorelines, or on low tidal grass flats, for example, and delve in depth into their daily life, their life cycles, their associations, and their relative place within the community.

All these guides are useful, and your bookshelves will soon overflow with them. Some will become old favorites and be referred to time and again. If you find one that is especially helpful when you go afield and that you take with you, buy a second copy to keep at home. Unfortunately good books do go out of print, and frequently used books do tend to wear out.

Although invertebrates look daunting at first, you may not classify many of them much further than order or family, which is relatively simple once you know that such a grouping exists. When it comes to separating the members of a single class, like birds or fish, into species, the going gets tougher. Members of different orders and families look much alike—a loon and a cormorant, a shearwater and a gull, or a bass and a perch are confusing until you have seen both and noted what then become obvious dissimilarities. Once down to the species level, the clues to distinguishing between them have to be sorted out based on subtle differences and it must be done quickly. You cannot take a bird home with you to look it up, nor can you stop a fleeing fish underwater long enough for relaxed reflection.

The success of some references is due to an arrangement which lets you get close quickly by emphasizing certain distinguishing features while ignoring others that have less diagnostic help, but which you are apt to concentrate on unless directed to do otherwise.

Stick with guides as regionally narrow as you can find. Too broad a base makes it confusing to use. The trouble is, the publisher wants as broad an audience as possible. As a result, many manuals put out by "big" publishers cover too much and not thoroughly enough. Look for local manuals in bookstores at the seashore, especially visitor centers in state and national seashore and wildlife refuges. Local bookstores are also likely to carry books on local lore put out by small presses that have a limited distribution.

Many a good guide is now out of print. Browsing used bookstores may help you find them, but an easier way is to look through the catalogs of booksellers who specialize in new and used books on nature, conservation, and the environment. (See references on page 156.)

Do not reject a book because its title seems too narrowly confined geographically. Among classic examples, long out-of-print works, and those written for publication by state museums are *Birds of Ohio, Wildflowers of New York,* and *Echinoderms of Connecticut.* Three more complete works would be hard to uncover, and their utility extends well beyond their state borders. More recently, Sterrer's *Marine Flora and*

Fauna of Bermuda is an example of a book that has wide application well beyond its appointed boundaries.

KEYS

Biologists resort to keys to separate out family, genus, and species whose differences are far from obvious and require closer anatomical examination. A key tells you what characteristic to look for and puts your choices into simple terms; either something is present or it's not, it has this or that, or it has one, two, or three whatever. From your selection at each step, you branch out to another characteristic, ignoring all other evidence. And on it goes, until you reach the genus or species that completely describes your specimen. If the key does not work, either you have incorrectly interpreted it; what you have isn't listed in it; or natural variation has struck again and interjected enough ambiguity to send you astray.

Generally, to follow an unfamiliar key you need the specimen before you. That usually means a moribund critter long pickled in Formalin or alcohol. You will quickly discern why color is rarely used in a key. The fluids and death itself have faded the remains to an ashen sameness that provides little help in identification.

For my own benefit, I once made up a key to Bermuda corals. Out of sixty species in the whole West Indies and environs, about twenty reside in Bermuda. Seven or eight can be recognized at a glance, but the rest, especially star and brain corals, look alike. The whole identification scheme I devised was based on their bleached bones. The key, which had ten branches, told you nothing about their live appearance or the color of their fleshy parts. First was the presence or absence of cups. The next chose between single and multiple cups. Branched or not then followed, then leaflike or not. By now twelve species had been identified, but those remaining had to be sorted out by the number of septa (vertical walls) per cup and the average diameter of the cup. Of course, once you know the corals, other differences will allow you to name them without going through this tedious exercise. The key will, however, save you from endlessly slogging between descriptions of species that may not even exist in your locale while looking for totally unfamiliar and unique points of separation.

Some keys go no further than family or genus. To proceed further may require the talents and gear of the specialist such as equipment that will cross-section your material and prepare tissues for microscopic examination and access to a specialized library. Unless you are connected with a university or otherwise have access to a specialized library, you may not be able to track down the arcane and inaccessible literature where its description may be buried.

The appendix contains a list of some of the better known identification guides and a few others that will be helpful. As you pick up more literature, look in their bibliographies for titles new to you. Older listings may be out of print; new titles appear constantly. "What's out there?" in the literature can be as much of a challenge as "What is it?" is in the field.

4

FIELD STUDY IN THE INTERTIDAL

No matter how intriguing an animal is, a complete view of it must include its neighbors and its surroundings. Pickled animals in vials have a place in systematics and structural biology, but offer few clues about the nature of that animal's existence. Knowing an animal's anatomy helps; you can infer what it might be capable of doing and where it might be capable of living, but functioning in its natural setting, the suitability of its structures assert themselves. Structure, behavior, and habitat are inextricably bound together into a working whole. The field is the place to see this and come to grips with each creature's entirety, for only by going to where its life is carried on daily, will you grasp the difficulties and opportunities confronting it and comprehend the grace of its adaptations.

For intertidal organisms, both air and water conspire to limit their range and life span. The rules for what lives where and for how long are set by degree of exposure, either to air from tidal change or to the buffeting of the water; to wave action, extremes in temperature, from freezing conditions in winter to searing heat in summer; to the physical and chemical condition of the water; for example, its dissolved oxygen content, its salinity, its turbidity (more or less the opposite of its clarity), pollution, and the character of the substrate.

When you go to the shoreline, go easy on collecting. Take only what you intend to use and do that sparingly. If you turn over a stone to see what is on the underside, roll it back in place before moving on. Anything growing on its upper surface will otherwise perish. If you seine, separate out what you want to save quickly and return the rest in enough time that they may survive.

If you think I am overstating the case, take a look at the mass destruction that can be done by a school class let loose on a beach. I have seen people take a quick look at a horseshoe crab, pulling it out of the shallows, then fling it high up on the beach where it is bound to needlessly die. A group seining will do much the same thing with netted fish. Others jam pails full of whatever their shovels turn up or what they catch only to let them sit under a hot sun and quickly suffocate.

Also keep in mind that most states or towns have shellfishing laws as to who can take shellfish, when, from where, and how many. Several states now require permits for collecting any sea creatures. Know your state and local laws before taking any specimens.

BEFORE YOU GO

When you have chosen a field site, create a sketch of the area from a map or chart as described earlier. If you cannot, be sure to make the sketch in the field before you leave. Once in the field, you will discover your outline chart is only an approximation of the landscape. Shoreline contours in sandy and muddy places, especially near the mouth of a stream or where the current is fast moving, change frequently. Unnavigable water holds little interest for the chartmaker, so that all very shoal, or shallow areas on charts are only rough guides.

Plan to carry a notebook with you. As your explorations progress, you may wish to numerically key in positions on your sketch and correlate them with your field entries; that is, the kind of bottom, dominant seaweed, typical animals, special finds and alike. Use a pencil; ink runs when wet and it is very easy to get your notebook wet.

Get a tide table that covers the area as close to your intended site as possible. High and low tide times can vary significantly within a few miles of coastline, so find the time difference between the closest reference point and the table itself. Table times and nearby reference points may differ by several hours, especially along tidal rivers, so you may either have to interpolate the time or determine it when you arrive at the site.

Tide tables generally list daily highs only. To find the lows, add six hours and twenty-five minutes to each high. Again, that difference may be affected by the presence of a river that holds back the incoming tidal flow on the flood and hastens it along the ebb.

Plan to arrive at your site on a falling tide, as many hours before as you expect to spend there as you do after the tide has turned. Thus, you can work your way out on the ebb and come back inshore on the flood. If the tides are extreme where you plan to work, plan out your route back thoroughly so that you do not wind up stranded on an offshore bar and have to swim for it or come in to a vanishing beach with nothing but a sheer cliff in front of you. If you are a stranger to the region, a few inquiries will help or, better yet, a few visits to the site at different tidal stages will give you a better idea of what you face.

Take along your camera. If you have not used it in a while, check to make sure your light meter is working and even if it is and you cannot remember when you last replaced its battery, get a new one. Choose a film with a speed commensurate with the brightness of the day and with your intended use of the pictures; that is, slides are fine to show to others, but prints can be mounted directly in your permanent notebook directly alongside whatever description and comments you choose to enter.

Plan to take close-ups. Most of what you will find is small and will fill the frame only if you either have a way to extend the distance between the lens and the film or change the apparent focal length of the lens. The latter can be done with supplementary lenses of different strengths. The former requires extension tubes or macro lens; both basically do the same thing.

If you know how to use fill-in electronic flash, take along your flash unit. If you have not used that unit in a while, replace its batteries. Fill-in flash gets rid of harsh shadows and properly used will greatly enhance the quality of your photos. If you have not used flash for close-ups get a how-to book and try it. Keep lots of notes; it is easy to repeat the same mistakes over and over again.

All camera equipment should be kept in a waterproof knapsack or shoulder bag along with a dry towel fitted to the outside of the bag. Salt water is corrosive and, given that you are sure to be picking things up as you go, you will need to dry your hands before you handle the camera.

Take along a flat, white, enamel pan (a photo tray, for instance) or a plastic tray to hold specimens for sorting and photography. Also bring along a plastic ruler to include in the photo to show the specimen's relative size. If you forget the ruler, a coin makes a good substitute.

Depending on the substrate, pack a hammer and chisel to remove specimens from rocks, a putty knife or scraper to remove specimens from pilings, and a shovel and sieves to retrieve specimens from sand or mud. For the latter, a two-gallon plastic pail with its bottom removed and replaced by ½-inch hardware cloth will do service both as a carrying container and as a sieve. The hardware cloth (galvanized wire mesh) can be held into the bottom of the pail with silicone caulking.

Carry assorted wide-mouth bottles and vials, all plastic if possible. If you do use glass (pint and quart jars made for canning are especially handy), make sure they are fitted with plastic caps. Also take along a few Zip-Loc bags. Where to put it all? Another two-gallon plastic bucket makes both a convenient carrier and can be pressed into use if you find an unusually large specimen.

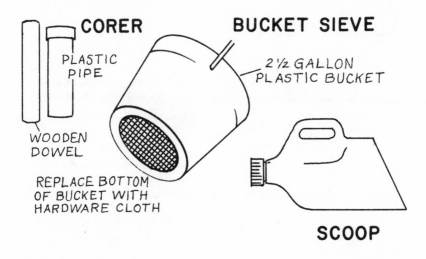

Collecting devices can be made from commonly available plastic utensils.

If you are planning to work in water more than a few inches deep, you cannot set a pail down without its natural buoyancy floating it and invariably spilling its contents. For shallow waters, fit a small, inflated inner tube or a styrofoam life-ring (available at a marine supply store) with a plastic laundry basket or a bucket, depending on the diameter of the float you choose. Affix a rope handle and you have a floating storehouse that can be used while wading or snorkeling.

A small aquarium dip net is useful to fetch a quick critter out of the shallows without doing it harm. A larger sweep net whose frame is strong enough to push through submerged marsh grass is sure to pick up a few shrimp and perhaps a small fish or two.

If you have an interest in the small creatures, or meiofauna as they are known (between 0.1 mm and 0.5 mm in length) that live between the grains of sand, take along a corer. It need be no more than an inch in diameter. A good one can be made from a plastic tube used by golf-

BUCKET FLOAT

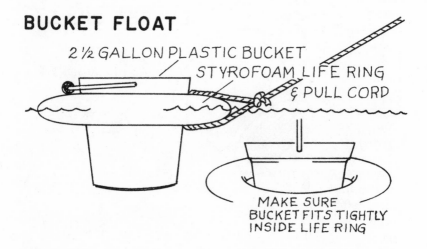

2 ½ GALLON PLASTIC BUCKET

STYROFOAM LIFE RING & PULL CORD

MAKE SURE
BUCKET FITS TIGHTLY
INSIDE LIFE RING

In knee-deep water a floating bucket comes in handy. Tie the pullcord to your belt.

ers to store practice balls. A length of plastic plumbing pipe with one end tapered by filing will also do, except the former tubing is translucent whereas the plumbing pipe is not. Simply push it vertically into the sand with a twisting motion to whatever depth you wish to explore, then withdraw it. Depending on the compactness of the strata, most of the time all but the very bottom of the core can be retrieved intact. It's handy to have a dowel that fits the inside diameter of the corer (a loose fit is best) to extract the core contents.

Segregate the core contents by depth; that is, the top inch or two in one jar, the next inch or two in another, and so forth. Add sea water immediately and shake gently. The animals living in the interstices between grains or clinging to the grains themselves cover a wide spectrum of life; nemertine worms, jaw worms, gastrotrichs, nematodes, rotifers, harpacticoid copepods, opisthobranch gastropods, small hydroids and polychaetes, and Kinorhynicha. All cannot be extracted by the same technique. However, the following method will retrieve most of them.

At home, you can separate the living material from the sand and organic matter by letting the jars of sand and water stand at room temperature for a few days to a few weeks; that is, until the water goes stale and shows signs of sulfiding (or more pragmatically put, until it begins to smell like rotten eggs). As the oxygen in the sand is depleted, the animals will migrate to the top layer of sand. Skim the top layer of sand off and put it in another jar. Add a magnesium sulfate solution (made by dissolving Epsom salts in tapwater until the density of the solution is equal to that of seawater, about 1.025 to 1.030, as measured with a hydrometer. See the chapter on aquaria for guidance on how to use a hydrometer) to the wet sand, stir gently, and wait ten minutes. Magnesium salts have a narcotic effect on many invertebrates and they will release their grip on the sand or cease moving when disturbed. Then gently swirl the sand-salt solution and either filter everything through coarse, plankton netting (or a nylon stocking) which will retain the sand but pass the organisms, or quickly decant off the supernatent from the sand. The sample is then ready for a look under a low-power microscope. See the chapter on microscopy for advice on further preservation.

Carry a low-power hand lens (6-10X) on a cord around your neck, a pair of inexpensive forceps (cheap or expensive, both rust fast), a pencil, pocket-sized notebook, and a wad of small, bond paper rectangles for temporary labels. (Write the location, date, and tentative identification on the paper and put the paper *in* the collection vial or bottle. It will keep for years and you can't smear or lose the labels as you can with inked, gummed labels on the outside of the jar.)

An odd item worth sticking in your pocket is a toothbrush, especially if you keep an aquarium. Poking along in the shallows, you are apt to come up with shells of clams covered with limey worm casings which appear to be dead but may not be. First make sure the shell is small enough to fit into a collection bottle. Then cut off all the attached algae with a paring knife. Finally, scrub the nooks and crannies of the shell with the toothbrush. This will remove trapped debris that can foul an aquarium. Keep the shell in fresh seawater and, with a hand lens, watch the tube openings for signs of life. The featherduster worms won't wait too long to expand and get back to the job of catching a meal.

If the water is cold, wear waders or hip boots. If it is really cold, wear long underwear. If the water is warm, wear an old pair of sneakers or sandals. Don't go barefoot; broken glass and sharp shells are everywhere.

If you plan to retrieve live specimens (and that should be your main goal), make sure your aquarium is up and running and ready to receive them. For their transportation home, bring along a plastic cooler and a battery-operated aerator, such as a unit used for aerating live bait. Don't crowd anything you want to keep alive and be sure to separate out creatures that don't get along well together (crabs don't get along well with anything, including other crabs).

IN THE FIELD

As you follow the falling tide, examine all you can, but remember to minimize your impact on the environment. Do not disturb habitats indiscriminately. If you move a rock, replace it as it was before you moved it. If you remove it from its original setting, return it to as close to where it was as you can. A sessile creature shifted to another zone in the intertidal cannot recorrect its position. Sort what you have found before you leave the site and return what you won't use to the sea.

You may want to anesthetize and kill your specimens immediately. Place the specimen in a plastic tray in sea water and allow it to expand. Carefully and slowly introduce a strong solution of Epsom salts. When the specimen no longer reacts to touch, add Formalin. Add enough to make the final solution 3 to 6% Formalin by volume. Formalin is a strong irritant and possible carcinogen (although many have doubts about its carcinogenic effects on humans), so be careful with it. When you can, replace the Formalin-seawater solution with 50% alcohol for long-term storage.

If you intend to keep your specimens alive but not in an aquarium, limit your collection to what you will be able to examine within the next few days. Again, don't crowd them and don't mix incompatible species.

BACK HOME

The amount you have collected should be tempered by the time you have after your field excursion to prepare and examine the material, especially live material and especially in warm weather.

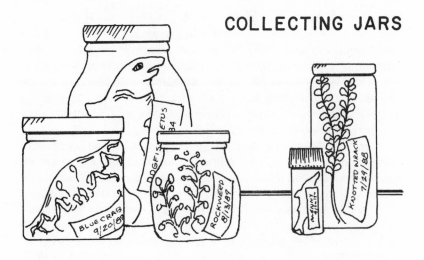

COLLECTING JARS

Remember to put the labels *inside* the jars. Avoid metal caps.

First, make notes on anything you observe on live specimens that won't keep long. Take photos of any specimens recently deceased (as with small fish) before their colors fade or they lose their shape. Even if you intend to preserve a specimen, take a photo before or shortly after its death. Coupled with the preserved carcass you will have a much better shot at what may prove to be a difficult identification.

Then complete and elaborate your field notes. Don't shirk this; what you have just done and seen is fresh in your mind, and as time passes you will never berate yourself for having written too much, but for writing too little. Each specimen or group of specimens should be recorded, showing the collecting locale, the date, habitat associations, and anything out of the ordinary that strikes you. If your identifications are doubtful, say so. Use a question mark to denote your uncertainty.

With repeated visits to the same locality you should be able to build up a list of its common species, and in what habitat they are normally found. If you return at seasonal intervals, you may be able to estimate their relative numbers. As difficult as this may seem, remember "many," "few," or "none" is informative.

ABOUT THE INTERTIDAL ZONE

Your initial field work should survey the common animals, plants, and kinds of habitats in the area. Return visits will probably find you concentrating on more specific habitats and a more limited fauna or flora.

You may find yourself curious about comparative differences among similar habitats that differ in some significant respect; for example, you might decide to study marshland life as you proceed up a saltwater river looking for the effects of declining salinity.

All animal life has common needs—oxygen, food, and an environment amenable to survival and reproduction. Oxygen is seldom a problem in a well-flushed intertidal zone. However, episodic industrial pollution or heavy sediment runoff may degrade or denude an area that otherwise looks reasonably normal. You may be able to either record the demise or recovery of such an area.

The common food sources for the grazers, scavengers, and small predators are floating plant debris, decomposing organic matter trapped in mud and sand sediments, bacteria, films of live algae and diatoms growing on mud, sand, and hard surfaces, and floating plankton. In turn, these creatures are fair game for larger predators—sea stars, sea anemones, fish, birds, and an occasional mammal. If you can uncover who eats what and some new force upsets either a key predator or prey, you may be able to trace its effects on others. Don't be surprised if nothing happens—the key predator hypothesis has taken a shellacking in recent years.

Breeding in temperate climes is attuned to temperature, and in some species, regulated by solar and lunar timetables. The shedding of eggs and sperm may be set with precision by the appearance of a full moon. Since many intertidal creatures release their reproductive products directly into the water where they drift with the currents, you can find these in plankton tows. To find a specific larval form will require many tows at different times of the day and night and at different times during the breeding season.

Some species lay single eggs or egg masses and usually attach them to firm surfaces. Check the stems of marsh grass, blades of kelp, underwater rock overhangs and nooks and crannies of all sorts. You can bring these back with you and watch them develop. Some eggs, buried in the sand, often blow ashore. The red knot, a seabird that makes a long migration each spring, times its arrival at Cape May, New Jersey with the egg-laying of the horseshoe crab. There are strands of beach where the tideline is green with their eggs. Put some eggs in a well-aerated jar with seawater and you can watch their whole development sequence through to hatching.

Life in the intertidal zone is harsh and full of sudden changes. The species in this environment are distributed according to their specific adaptations, which allow them to survive a variety of perils.

Massive rock and boulders suit the clingers, and if the rock is soft enough like sandstone, some borers. Cobbles and pebbles have the fewest inhabitants; rolling stones make for hard living. Sand, mud, and clay serve those who dig in, who then either feed from the waters over them or take their needs from the surrounding silts.

The degree of wave exposure is a major sorting factor in determining which animal and plant life will thrive; it is closely coupled with the kind of substrate available to that life. Severe currents carry away all those who can't hang on, moving everything animate or inanimate, leaving only the hardiest clingers and burrowers. If the sand is on the move in the locale, little can tolerate its continuous scouring and smothering effects.

Tidal exposure limits diversity either by desiccation or temperature extremes. The presence of one species can be mandatory for the presence of many others. For example, kelp will withstand desiccation and will support a host of other life simply by providing protection from drying, sudden temperature shifts, and predation.

The availability of oxygen, changes in salinity, and the amount of light have profound effects on intertidal life. Fish driven into shallows on a hot day by predators can quickly perish from oxygen depletion. Harbors beset by oxygen-robbing wastewater will have little or no bottom dwelling life. Fresh water runoff from higher-than-normal rainfalls can wipe out species who cannot tolerate low salinities. Constant silting, invariably caused by man's disruption of the coastline, can lower light levels to a point where sea grasses will no longer grow; witness the vast decline in eelgrass beds in Chesapeake Bay as an example.

Predation by birds, man, and occasional marine visitors can significantly reduce the numbers of a particular species and alter its distribution. On the east coast the horseshoe crab migrates inshore in late spring and eats juvenile clams. The spotty nature of clam beds has been attributed to these seasonal intrusions.

COLLECTING SEAWEED

Every tide flat and shoreline has its dominant seaweeds. Aside from looking over their stipes for small specimens, you may wish to make a permanent collection of them. Gather up and keep your specimens in a bucket of clean seawater. When you are ready to mount them, transfer them, one at a time, to a shallow tray of *fresh* water. Spread out the specimen and arrange it in an approximation of its natural shape. Slide a sheet of herbarium mounting paper under the specimen and gently ease it out of the tray while maintaining the shape you want.

When you are satisfied with its arrangement, place the mounting paper on a sheet of blotting paper and cover it with plastic wrap or waxed paper. Place another sheet of blotting paper over the plastic wrap. Sandwich the whole thing between two sheets of corrugated cardboard and put it into a plant press. You can mount several specimens in the press at one time. Clamp down the press and let the whole thing sit for a week to dry. Once dry, label the specimens and cover them with fresh plastic wrap or cellophane. Store flat.

PLANT PRESS

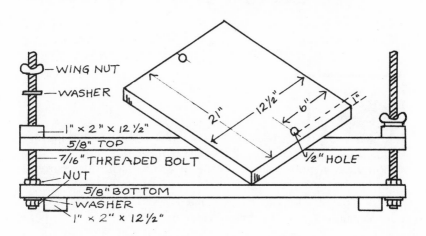

If carefully stacked and interleaved, a press can hold a dozen specimens.

HOW TO MAKE A PLANT PRESS

Standard herbarium sheets are 11½-by-16½ inches. Cut two pieces of ¾-inch exterior grade plywood to 12½-by-21 inch. If you wish, you can affix 1-by-2 inch strips along the short ends of each piece of plywood for reinforcement.

On the lengthwise centerline of the plywood, one inch from the edge at either end, drill ½ inch diameter holes. Using cut-down 7/16-inch threaded rods (or long, fully threaded bolts), nuts, and washers permanently affix two rods, 12 inches long, upright in one (the bottom) piece of plywood. After loading the press, put the other piece of plywood on top, and with washers and wing nuts, tighten it down. If you plan to use the press frequently, give the wood a couple of coats of marine spar varnish to protect it from moisture.

Herbarium paper is a specialty item and not easy to obtain in small quantities. Art supply houses stock 100% cotton rag, acid-free, heavy-weight paper that will do nicely as a substitute.

5

FIELD STUDY AT SEA

I f you can find a way to get offshore, either on your own boat or on a charter boat, you can extend your opportunities for observing and collecting to a much wider range of animal life.

What is possible for you to do is limited by your means and mode of transportation. If you go out for a day of fishing on a large party boat, few, if any, of the captain's customers will appreciate anything that interferes with their chances of catching fish. Obviously you can photograph fish brought aboard or watch sea birds with binoculars, but it is unlikely you can put simple sampling equipment overboard without upsetting someone. If you sight a whale or a school of porpoises do not expect the skipper to chase after them for a closer look. To do so might risk losing his repeat customers.

Unless you own a boat, your best bet is to go out with a small group on a charter boat that is limited to six paying passengers. Make sure your companions and the skipper understand what you want to do and know how long it will take you to do it.

Before you go, find out what kind of fishing the skipper has planned—from an anchored position, by drifting, or by trolling. You may be able to work a small dredge or tow a plankton net without interfering with the rest of the party. Obviously, if you are trolling for tuna at ten knots you can forget doing much work over the side, and the trip will be, from your point of view, a waste of time.

Also, be sure that whatever you want put over the side and retrieve can be done without damaging any trim and whatever you bring aboard can be sorted and stored without getting muck all over the deck. A sheet of tough reinforced plastic, the kind used for boat covers, or heavy canvas may be needed to protect rails and the deck.

If the charter boat specializes in taking out scuba divers (invariably to shipwreck sites) you will be reasonably free to operate whatever gear you choose while the divers are underwater.

A dive boat captain is seldom as fussy about the condition of the afterdeck as a charter fishing captain. A dive boat deck must withstand repeated blows from dropped dive weights, air tanks, and heavy pieces of ship's parts retrieved as souvenirs (which often ooze a black goo that smells like rotten eggs).

If a sea is running and the boat is anchored you can set out a plankton net. The forward motion of the sea will perform the same function as a slow tow.

If you want bottom samples of sand or mud, you can ask a diver to scoop up a bucketful for you. Go forward to the bow (most divers descend via the anchor line) and lower a galvanized iron pail attached by a clothesline somewhat longer than the amount of anchor line out. Don't use a plastic bucket—it is a poor scoop on a compacted bottom. The diver can take the pail down with him, fill it, give a few tugs on the line, and let you haul it to the surface.

An understanding diver can also take a few grab samples for you and whatever else that can be conveniently collected that you might be interested in. However, resist the urge to ask for too much. Remember, the diver has his or her own agenda and dive time is brief and expensive.

If the surface water is reasonably clear you will want to go snorkeling. In the fall months along the northeast coast, gyres of clear, warm, Gulf Stream water separate off from the mainstream and drift within five to ten miles from the coastline. These waters contain a marvelous assortment of large planktonic forms, as well as an occasional exotic tropical fish.

If the idea of snorkeling at sea is appealing, consider the purchase of a wet suit to keep you warm for long periods of water exposure. Wet suits range in thickness from ⅛-inch to ¼-inch and are designed for a wide range of water temperatures and activities. A thin "shorty" vest will extend your time in 80°F water for a while, but a long-sleeved wet suit top will keep you warm indefinitely (if you are too warm you can

SIMPLE DREDGES

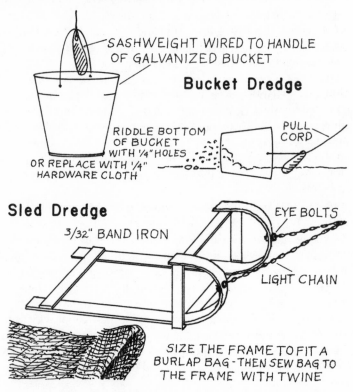

SASHWEIGHT WIRED TO HANDLE OF GALVANIZED BUCKET

Bucket Dredge

RIDDLE BOTTOM OF BUCKET WITH ¼" HOLES OR REPLACE WITH ¼" HARDWARE CLOTH

PULL CORD

Sled Dredge

3/32" BAND IRON

EYE BOLTS

LIGHT CHAIN

SIZE THE FRAME TO FIT A BURLAP BAG - THEN SEW BAG TO THE FRAME WITH TWINE

Dredging will greatly extend the depth to which you can collect. The bucket dredge can be used at the end of a pier or jetty for as far as you can fling it.

always open the front zipper). In water 55° to 60°F you need a full top, bottom, and boots. Below 55°F you also need a hood and gloves. Below 45°F, the whole outfit had best be ¼-inch rubber. Any well-equipped dive shop can help you make a selection.

WHALEWATCHING

Naturalist cruises to watch whales or sea birds (if the captain can't find whales) have grown in popularity over the last ten years. These cruises are seasonal, for they depend on the habits of each whale species.

In summer and fall, you can count on fin whales and humpback whales to show up on Stellwagen Bank off Provincetown, Massachusetts. It is a summer feeding ground for these whales (and occasionally a few other species) who chase the sand launce and other species that inhabit those waters. The whales visit so regularly that a whale-watching industry has sprung up in seaside towns within a few hour's cruising time from the bank.

Along the California coast, the annual migration of gray whales to and from their breeding grounds off the Baja Peninsula draws most of the whale-watchers, although other species turn up regularly in Puget Sound and along other sections of the coast. You can watch gray whales from shore, find a day boat that will put you in closer proximity, or sign up for a week's trip out of San Diego to the lower Baja coast during their breeding season.

Some trips are half-day, open boat; that is, first come, first serve. Others are chartered to groups and you must make arrangements in advance. If you don't know whether you can see whales locally or whether anyone runs whale sightseeing trips, ask at the aquarium nearest you. In a few places, the local chamber of commerce tourist bureau may know of them.

Keep in mind that because whales appeared at a particular location the previous year, there is no ironclad guarantee they will show up again this year. It all depends on the food supply. For example, the humpback whales that feed on fish off Stellwagen Bank can just as well go to more northerly waters (as some of the Atlantic stock do) off Nova Scotia and Labrador. Before you travel a long distance, find out if regular sightings are common.

Before you go, also find out what whales you are likely to see and bone up on their identification. Same thing with birds. Looking it up during the general excitement of a sighting coupled with the tendency of a boat to roll when the engines are slowed calls for more hands (one for the rail, one for binoculars or camera) than you are apt to have available.

Since the bulk of the whale is below the waterline, identification is not as easy as the full-drawing illustrations given in books would suggest. They can, however, be identified by a combination of clues—their waterline shape, the presence or absence of a dorsal fin, the shape and height of their blow, their diving form, and their swimming behavior.

Unless the sea is flat calm, which is rare, wear rain gear or a big, water-resistant windbreaker—big enough to tuck your binoculars or camera into should a sheet of spray slat across the deck. If you tend to get seasick or if you overdid it the night before, remember to take sea-sickness pills *before* you leave the dock. Once ill, they are useless.

YOUR OWN BOAT

If you own a boat you are limited only by its offshore capabilities, range, and storage capacity. If you wish, you can rig an A-frame to lift a heavy dredge, a bottom grab, or a piston corer, if you can figure out how to borrow or otherwise obtain these rather expensive oceanographic devices. You can rig a boarding ladder and take along a pair of divers (never one singly) who will agree to gather samples for you in exchange for a free trip. You can set out a longline, a gillnet, or tow a miniature otter trawl. However, otter trawls and other specialized fishing equipment, even small research varieties, are expensive. Also, you must check out state laws to see if by using this kind of gear you fall into the category of a commercial fisherman and if so, just what that entails.

If your main interest is bottom fauna, either creatures living on the bottom (epifauna) or in the bottom (infauna which are usually subdivided by size into macrofauna, creatures larger than 0.5 mm or meiofauna, those less than 0.5 mm) you will be forced by necessity to limit your sampling to a working depth of 100 feet or less, about the limit for sport scuba diving. To sample much deeper requires winches, big spools of cable, and heavy retrieval gear. At 50 feet, a diver can push a corer in the sediment by hand and retrieve it with little or no trouble. At 500 feet, you must lower a very heavy device to the bottom that will then drive a corer into the bottom by its sheer mass. Next, you must winch the whole assembly up to the deck; all in all, a daunting prospect on a small boat. Even taking a shallow scoop of top sediment at such a depth requires a Peterson grab or like instrument which is heavy, and once set, dangerous to operate.

Other than the freedom to go when and where you please, a significant advantage to your own boat is its storage capacity. You can carry a great deal of gear for opportunistic use: a dip-net, a plankton net, a dredge, snorkeling gear, underwater listening devices, a camera or video equipment, artificial lighting, aquaria, storage pails and aerating equipment to transport captured material to a home aquarium alive, chemical preservatives, trays for sorting materials before bringing them home, a simple microscope for pre-sorting; in short, a floating field lab.

Some of the techniques applicable for use from a small boat have or will be mentioned in preceding or subsequent chapters and will not be repeated here. Collections from the sea can be handled in much the same manner as collections from the intertidal. As with intertidal species, specimens from the sea are best examined alive. Many are short-lived once removed from their natural environment.

Because many creatures are too large to take to a home aquarium (a shark, for example), or are too fragile (a pelagic jellyfish, for one), or won't do well in a small aquarium (a mackerel, for instance), your only record of them, other than a written description, will be a photograph.

NIGHT LIFE

Your own boat will give you an opportunity to tow for plankton at night and see a cast of characters different from those that turn up in daytime tows. Depending on the time of year and the water temperature, you may also see a considerable amount of bioluminescence which emanates from planktonic animals that sink well below the surface in daytime.

At night, a light in the water strung over the side and suspended by a short line, usually attracts fish, squid, and invertebrates. The longer it is left on, the bigger the creatures drawn to it as the opportunity to prey on the early arrivals is sensed.

In southern waters, a light on the waters often leads to fish leaping well above the surface. Either they are chasing baitfish or are somehow excited by the beam. If you have a dip-net you can often attract them close enough to use it.

LISTENING IN

The underwater world is not a quiet place. You don't hear much underwater only because your ears are not designed to pick up the multitude of noises below. If you want to hear the songs of the humpback whale, the clicks of porpoises, the grunts of fish, or any of the hundreds of other sounds produced by things living and inanimate, it lies within your means to do so.

You will need a battery-operated tape recorder, cable that will with-

stand the rigors of the sea, and a hydrophone. Commercial hydrophones are expensive, but you can make your own if you can manufacture a few small parts and wire up a few simple circuits.

Long before Roger Payne began analyzing the musical phrasings of
humpbacks, Frank Watlington, a sound detection specialist who spent
many years on Bermuda working for the United States government, developed a series of low-cost listening devices that any amateur can duplicate. His early devices were reviewed in *Scientific American*'s "Amateur Scientist" in October 1960, March 1964, and August 1970.

The heart of a hydrophone is a pressure transducer, a device that
turns variations in acoustical pressure into an electrical signal. Watlington's early hydrophones were magnetostriction transducers, basically a
coil of insulated wire wrapped longitudinally around a tube of nickel;
nickel's magnetic properties are altered when it is subjected to stress.
When a current is applied to the coil, a magnetic field is set up which

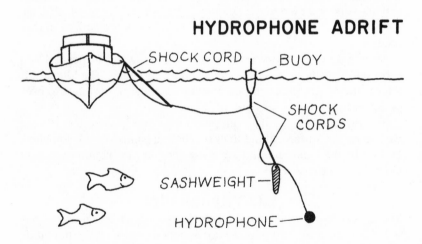

HYDROPHONE ADRIFT

A major problem in recording sound underwater is the noise generated
by the tether line jerking the hydrophone.

permanently magnetizes the nickel. If the nickel is stressed by sound, the permanent magnetic field is weakened. When the stress is relieved, the magnetic field revives to its former strength. The advantage to this kind of hydrophone is that it is very responsive from 200 to 10,000 Hertz (Hz) but poor below 100 Hz. Although you will miss many natural, low frequency sounds, you also avoid cable and 60 Hz noise.

Watlington's later hydrophones used ceramic piezoelectric transducers. A piezoelectric device produces a current when stressed. Except for some simple machining, these are easier to assemble than the magnetostriction devices and cover a wider frequency range.

How to assemble the transducer, provide impedance matching, enclose the unit (in a plastic ketchup bottle filled with castor oil), fit cable, and deploy it in such a way as to avoid boat and wave noise is all covered in his book, *How to Build and Use Low-Cost Hydrophones,* available from TAB Books, Blue Ridge Summit, PA, 17214.

6

MARINE FISH

The habits and habitats of fish, their numbers, and migrations are all subjects of interest to the marine naturalist who, like the professional fisheries biologist, must often make inferences from limited evidence.

You can contribute by fish tagging, reporting unusual occurrences, and by conducting regular surveys repeatedly at specific places. If tragedy strikes in the form of a fish kill, you can quantify it by determining the species, numbers, and area affected. These data could prove helpful in monitoring later recovery.

You can investigate the seasonal distribution of young fish in an estuary by catching and releasing them with a seine, a baitfish trap, or whatever means at your disposal that will give you a numerical measure of their abundance.

By examining the stomach contents of a few under a microscope, you can tell what they have been eating. By looking over their gills and skin you can tell what parasites are bothering them. You can also ascertain whether they are suffering diseases like fin rot which suggests they are swimming in polluted water.

Your first order of business is to learn the rudiments of the structure, physiology, and habits of fish—their anatomy, how they swim, breathe, breed, and sense their surroundings, what they eat, as well as their likely whereabouts during their lifetime.

Next, find out what species of fish inhabit the waters that interest you and look up their life histories as well as how to identify them. When you actually catch some of them, you may find you have difficulties identifying them, especially since juveniles and fry do not always look like their parents and are hardly ever mentioned in popular guide-books. You may want to write to the Fish and Wildlife Service for information on certain species, check identifications with a state or federal fisheries biologist, or, if really stuck, write the Smithsonian Institute for advice.

FISH SURVEYS

If you are a scuba diver and repeatedly visit specific underwater sites—rock outcrops, shipwrecks, towers and such—you can visually tally the kinds and numbers of fish that frequent there and watch the seasonal changes in their distribution.

If you are a member of a local fishing club or have a good relationship with several party boat skippers, you can keep track of the seasonal comings and goings of recreational species. If you know a commercial fisherman, you can do much the same for commercial species, and if he will cooperate, you can get an idea of the size of catches relative to the fishing effort expended. If you can spend some time on his boat from one season to the next, by measuring the length and weight of a sample of his catch you can get an indication of the condition of the stock and changes from year to year.

Inshore, you can survey jettys and sea walls as well as benthic substrates by snorkeling. To do this, identify and count all the free-swimmers on the first pass. Leave the counts of those fish that hide in crevices and burrows, hug the bottom, or hover over rocks and wreckage for your return trip.

Use common sense about conducting a survey along a jetty, wall, or coral reef that suffers heavy surf. If you are physically capable of handling such a rough environment, keep in mind there are times you cannot muscle against the force of a sudden heavy wave no matter what your strength. You must outmaneuver it by using it to keep yourself out of danger. As you are thrust forward you must learn to tuck-turn so that you are oriented feet forward and flippers first. Thus you will be able to ward off the upcoming obstruction with your legs, not your head; not stiff-legged, but in such a way that you absorb the shock as you would when landing from a fall. As the wave recedes you can then immediately push yourself out with it. Wear a wet suit to protect your body from abrasion and chilling.

For night surveys, a long bottom line over the survey path will be a big help. Working at night takes at least three people; two in the water and one standing by on land or in a boat. If you work from shore, one diver should tow a diver's flag and an illuminated marker beacon (the ones made for life jackets work well). The other diver should keep in contact with the first by either a buddy line or by holding on to another float line. Should either diver get separated, simply surface and go to the float.

One way of surveying in deep water either for fish or plankton is to buoy a line to a heavy weight, and at set intervals (say every 20 feet down) to whatever you feel is a safe operating depth (do not exceed 100 feet even if you are an experienced scuba diver), provide a ring from which you can attach a 100-foot tether (clothesline works well). Thus several divers can operate in a 200-foot diameter circle at their assigned depths without getting physically separated from each other.

When working from a boat, make sure the boat is well anchored, manned, and at night, well illuminated. Make certain that whomever mans the boat knows how to operate it. Also make sure they pay attention to where you and your buddy are located. Prearrange emergency signals. At night each diver should be carrying both a waterproof light and a whistle. Either should be used to attract the attention of the boat. If the boat tender wants the divers back on board, the universal way to signal them is to start the engine.

Surveys in shallow water can also be conducted by slowly towing a snorkeler with a boat. You can rig the end of a towline with a diving plane for easier descent and ascent. The snorkler calls out what has been seen and a second person (not the helmsman) records it. This method has proven especially helpful for reef flat surveys in shallow, tropical waters.

In bays, estuaries, tidal flats, and shallows where the water is too murky for visual observations by snorkling, fish populations can be estimated by seining. It's a two-person job. Good results can be had with a 40-foot-by-4-foot seine with 3/16-inch meshes. You will miss the adults and faster sub-adults, but you will catch some sub-adults and juveniles. Haul the seine parallel to the shoreline for a set distance, then turn the outward end shoreward and beach the catch. Know the bottom contours; the offshore person should not be put in danger of unexpectedly dropping into a hole. As an alternative, both can wade off the beach, spread the net, and walk it into the shallows.

Sort and count the catch as quickly as you can. Except for unidentified species and malformed or diseased fish, return the rest to the sea as soon as you are able. Keep several buckets of seawater handy; one for the fish you cannot identify, a second for the occasional rarity that you may want for your aquarium, and a third for all the rest of the fish. Gently transfer fish from the net into the bucket to make a rapid estimate of their numbers, then release them into the water. You may turn up more oddities in one season than in others. In the temperate summer and autumn of the mid-Atlantic coast, the warm ring Gulf Stream water carries many a tropical fish shoreward and the diligent seiner can snare these strays for an aquarium.

Pickle the malformed or diseased fish in a 3% Formalin-seawater solution, as well as one or two of those fish you cannot immediately iden-

UNDERWATER TOWPLANE

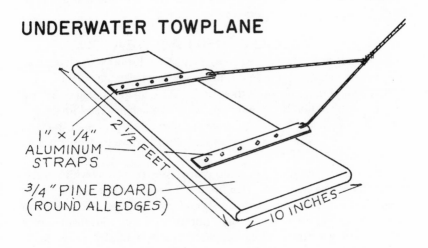

1" × 1/4"
ALUMINUM
STRAPS

2 1/2 FEET

3/4 " PINE BOARD
(ROUND ALL EDGES)

10 INCHES

Grab the board with both hands on the leading edge near the straps. To dive force the leading edge downward.

tify. Close-up photos of each species and fish in unusual condition can come in handy later on for getting answers via correspondence, for example. If you put the dead fish on a hard-foam, plastic board, spread its fins and pin them in an open position, then douse it with Formalin; the fins will remain erect when you remove the pins making a subsequent photo much more useful for identification.

You can prepare to take fish photos by constructing a simple platform made of wood and glass that will allow you to place the fish on the glass and allow you to put a piece of colored paper beneath it for background at a distance far enough away from the fish that it is out of focus. Be sure and include a ruler in the scene to indicate scale.

Try to repeat your tows at regular intervals, say biweekly for a year or at least in the less hostile part of the year, April through November. This will show seasonality patterns. If you and members of a volunteer team continue this for several years, you can provide a sound (and often, only) picture of the state of the environment where you have been sampling. One such group did repeated surveys at ten sites around the Raritan Bay estuary, a body of water recovering from years of abuse. They found that twenty-seven species resided there, and that it was an active and productive nursery for many others.

ABOUT FISH AT SEA

Schooling fishes spawn annually, thus produce distinct year-class progeny whose lengths and weights cluster about an average. As they grow older, natural mortality thins their ranks. Thus, all else being equal, we would expect to find larger numbers of smaller fish in a random sample of a fish population, but in nature this pattern rarely prevails. Large and small fish rarely school together; older fish may move to deeper waters or migrate away.

Because of natural events, some year-classes do poorly while others succeed exceptionally well. That implies the lengths and weights of the same species, randomly sampled, should reveal the relative success of each succeeding year-class. It may, but the difficulty with that concept lies in getting a truly random sample. Fish school by size, occasionally in mixed species, and thus segregate themselves in the sea. Even if all sizes freely intermingle, the way you catch them usually biases the size sampled; that is, the little ones escape through the net meshes and the bigger, faster ones outswim the net and thus are not sampled.

What size, weight (total body weight, weight of reproductive organs, weight of fat storage such as the relative size of the liver in sharks), and age do reveal is the state of health of the year-classes. For example, the dressed weight of swordfish caught commercially has dropped nearly in half over the last ten years, a sign that their average age is younger, a result of serious overfishing of that species.

FISH TAGGING

If you catch fish and can identify them, measure their length, note when and where they were caught, tag them, and release them; the returns will help point out their migration patterns and their rate of growth.

The American Littoral Society maintains the largest private tagging enterprise in the United States. You can purchase tags and tagging implements for a nominal fee from them. The kit explains how to tag (it requires inserting a sharp, hollow needle in the back of the fish just under the end of the first set of dorsal fins, threading through a numbered tag that contains a return address imprinted on it, then removing the needle and loosely tying the ends of the plastic tag. Hints on handling the fish to make sure it lives when returned to the water are included.)

Obviously, that particular kind of tag won't work for shark or billfish. Amateur naturalists who are also deep-sea fishermen have tagged those species for the National Marine Fisheries Service. Again, the American Littoral Society can provide you with the names and addresses of those currently seeking volunteer help.

If you intend to tag shark, find someone who is doing it and try to get out with him. It's tricky and requires the help of several people to do properly. Also, identifying sharks is not easy, and the more you see them in the presence of someone who knows them, the quicker you will pick up the subtle differences that distinguish one species from another. The American Littoral Society sponsors shark-tagging trips; that might be a good way of getting started.

WEIGHT, LENGTH, AND SEX

Getting measurements from a few fish presents no problem, but handling fish in quantity, measuring and weighing them quickly, and keeping records straight calls for pre-planning and organization.

For weighing, the hanging type of spring scales are the easiest to use

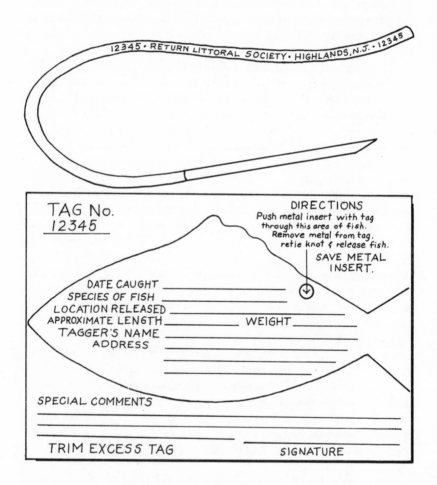

12345 · RETURN LITTORAL SOCIETY · HIGHLANDS, N.J. · 12345

TAG No.
12345

DIRECTIONS
Push metal insert with tag
through this area of fish.
Remove metal from tag,
retie knot & release fish.

SAVE METAL
INSERT.

DATE CAUGHT _____
SPECIES OF FISH _____
LOCATION RELEASED _____
APPROXIMATE LENGTH _____ WEIGHT _____
TAGGER'S NAME _____
ADDRESS _____
_____
_____

SPECIAL COMMENTS
_____
_____
TRIM EXCESS TAG _____
SIGNATURE

on a boat where rolling might affect both the ease of use and accuracy of a platform scale. Check the scales with known weights in the range you are measuring. These known weights can be as simple as beanbags of lead shot weighed by your grocer on a scale that has been checked by a food inspector. If your scale shows an error, note it on your data sheet and provide a spare column to enter the corrected weights after the job is done. Don't try to correct each weight as you read it.

For length, use a measuring board. You can make one from a piece of 8-inch wide pine, ¾-inch thick, and a bit longer than the biggest fish you intend to measure; certainly no longer than 2½ to 3 feet (if you do come across something longer, use a tape measure). Dado a groove down the middle of the board to receive a cut-down meter stick. At the head end, zero on the meter stick, attach a noseboard about 3 inches high. Glue the meter stick in the board and give the whole thing a few coats of spar varnish.

To measure a fish, lay it on the board with its nose butted up against the noseboard. Read its length at the fork of the tail. If the tail has no fork, read it at the end of its tail fin.

The sex of some species of fish can be told from external appearance. For example, male winter flounders have a rough caudal peduncle on the underside; females are smooth. For others, you will have to gut the fish and examine its reproductive organs. Ovaries are generally reddish or orange, grainy, and large; testes tend to be white, elongated, and small. Naturally this means destroying the fish. Ask yourself if your project justifies their sacrifice and if it does, what is the smallest sample size that will yield meaningful data.

AGE: SCALES AND OTOLITHS

The age of a fish can be found by several techniques. A time series of length-frequency distributions is often coupled with tag return data, growth rings on scales, or growth patterns in other bony parts of their body, particularly otoliths. Sometimes cross-sections of fin rays and vertebrae are used. What method is used depends on the species. For example, using growth ring counts on scales, described below, can be confounded by "false annuli" in some species. Check your method and results with a fisheries biologist, either state or federal.

The lengths of great numbers of the same species from local waters, when grouped by frequency of length, can show distinct peaks. For

FISH MEASURING BOARD

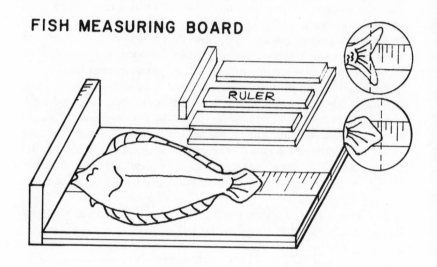

RULER

For a few fish you could as easily use a tape measure affixed to the boat rail but a board is much more convenient and accurate for a lot of fish.

young fish, each peak can be attributed to a specific year-class. But yearly increases in size slow down as the fish approach maturity and the data gathered from such groups fails to distinguish age differences.

For some bony fish from temperate and colder waters, scales can be used for telling age; examples include flounders, haddock, sea bass, drum, and scup. Teleosts either have thin, transparent, spiny ctenoid scales or spineless cycloid scales. Some species have both and both contain annuli. The space between each heavy ring, or annulus, indicates a season's growth. Obviously growth rings are not present in warm water fish who grow continuously. Neither the scales of cartilaginous fish nor the thick scales of gars and sturgeons are useful as growth indicators, nor are the annuli in all bony fish distinct enough to be counted.

Near the center of either a ctenoid or a cycloid scale lies a clear patch called the focus, the point from which the scale originated. Concentric

FISH SCALE   OTOLITH

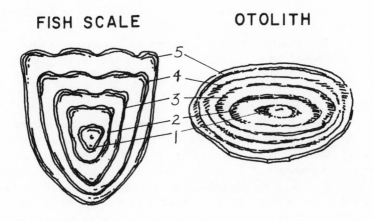

Determining the age of a fish either by scale or by otolith is not always as easy as this drawing would make it appear.

circuli lie in ridges, like map contours, around the focus. Flexure lines, called radii, emanate outward from the focus. At intervals, lie crowded circuli, called annuli. A single annulus is the discontinuity created by slow growth in autumn and winter followed by rapid growth in spring and summer. Each species has its own peculiarities in shape and form. Reading annuli accurately takes experience.

SCALE PROCEDURE

- Take ctenoid scales (normally fish with spiny rays) near the tip of the pectoral fin.
- Take cycloid scales (usually soft-rayed fish) in the area between the dorsal fin and the lateral line.
- Remove several scales with forceps or knife blade.

- Clean the scales with water. You can temporarily mount them in water or glycerin for an immediate look under the microscope or dry them and make either a permanent microscope mount or a slide projection mount.
- Sandwich the scale between two microscope slides, tape the ends, and examine with a microscope.
- You can also view scales by mounting them between 2-by-2 inch glass slides and projecting them with a 35-mm projector. Use a tiny touch of glue to hold each scale in place. Cardboard mounts and clear plastic cut to 35 mm size can also be used in a similar manner.

OTOLITH PROCEDURE

Growth layers in otoliths can also be used to tell the age of fish and is the preferred method for alewives, herring, mackerel, cod, pollack, hakes, butterfish, and goosefish. Three pairs of otoliths (calcified earbones) lie side by side at the rear of the brain, in chambers called sacculi which lie along the fish's plane of bilateral symmetry. One of the pairs is much larger than the other two pairs and that is the pair to use. Because the brain is encased in bone, getting to the otoliths requires a sharp, strong knife and in some especially hard heads, a saw.

Make a transverse, backward sloping cut behind the eyes (how far behind must be found out by experience) through the base of the brain case to the gill cover. Bend the head forward. This should expose the brain. With flounder, cut through the ridge of bone between the eyes to the gill cover. Don't cut deeply, just clear the bone. Open the cut. The otoliths lie one above the other in flounder.

Otoliths vary in shape among species; they lengthen and thicken with age. Growth zones in flat, thin otoliths can be determined by viewing them magnified with transmitted light. Thick otoliths must be cross-sectioned with a jeweler's saw and viewed by reflected light. Because the growth layers consist of alternate layers of aragonite and protein, burning the surface with an open flame, thus charring the protein, can enhance differences between the layers. Growth patterns are not symmetrical in all species and vary with age, making some difficult to interpret.

Telling the age of fish from scales or otoliths is worth a few practice trials on purchases from the fish market. However, to be meaningful in field work it must be performed on large numbers. Not only is this tedious work, but the value of it in the light of destroying a catch that might have survived to a ripe old age is a matter worth considering.

TRANSPORTING LIVE FISH

During seining, tidepooling, or diving, you may have the opportunity to collect fish for your aquarium. To enhance your success and their chances of survival you must heed a few simple rules.

Have your aquarium set up, running, and "balanced" (more about that in the chapter on aquariums). A separate quarantine tank is prudent if your main tank is large and prospering.

Handle fish gently with a dip-net; their skin is easily abraded once out of water. Some fish lose their scales at the slightest provocation. Either condition makes them susceptible to infection. Transfer them from the seine to your seawater container with a dip-net. Avoid grabbing them; if you must, use wet hands.

In hot weather, even for a few fish and short distances, plan to hold them in an insulated container. An inexpensive styrofoam cooler with a tight-fitting lid will do.

You can use either an "open" or "closed" system for supplying oxygen. If you are using a car, use an open system; by air freight, a closed system.

For an open system, put the fish in a plastic bag filled about a third of the way with water, and set it in the cooler. Insert an air stone and hose into the bag and seal the bag loosely with a rubber band. Be sure to prop the bag up so that it cannot spill in the cooler. Another bag with a little ice will slowly cool the whole system, but don't overdo it and kill the fish with a sudden chill. The air to the stone can be supplied from a portable battery-operated pump which can be obtained from a bait shop or you can use a pump designed to work from your car's cigarette lighter socket.

For a closed system, saturate the water holding the fish with oxygen from an oxygen cylinder by passing it into the water through an air stone. You can get small cylinders of oxygen from a medical supply store. Also fill the remainder of the plastic bag with oxygen and seal it. (Warning! Do not use oxygen near an open flame or near a glowing object; oxygen supports combustion with a vengeance.)

For both open and closed systems, adding a buffer that will control the pH of the water, and therefore the carbon dioxide tension level, will enhance chances of survival. Accumulation of carbon dioxide is more likely to cause mortalities than low oxygen, especially for long trips or crowded transport tanks. An organic buffering agent called tris (hydroxymethyl) aminomethane or TRIS, for short, is used. Purchased as a free base and dissolved in water, its initial pH is too high; that is, the solution is too alkaline. Therefore, it is necessary to mix it with an acid to partly neutralize it. The ideal pH for the salt water is 8.2 to 8.3. McFarland and Norris in *The Control of pH in Fish Transport* (California Fish and Game 44 (4) pp. 291–310 (1958)), suggest two to five grams of buffer per gallon of seawater. Use the lower amount for brief trips and few fish, and the larger for air shipments or crowded tanks. The authors say many species are unaffected by as much as twenty grams per gallon of buffer.

TRIS is a stable powder easily dissolved in seawater. Citric acid is also a dry powder and a convenient source of acid. Proper mixtures of TRIS and citric acid can be pre-mixed and pre-packaged for field use.

For an initial pH of 8.20, the ratios of the two ingredients in grams per gallon for seawater are:

TRIS	Citric Acid
2	0.63
5	2.00
10	6.95
20	15.80

You can also use hydrochloric acid and a pH meter to set the dissolved buffer. TRIS and citric acid are available from Sigma Chemical Company, P.O. Box 14508, St. Louis, MO 63178. Citric acid, C0759, is sold in one-kilo lots and TRIS, Sigma 7-9, T1378, in 500-gram lots. Also ask them for Bulletin 106B, for a fuller description of ratios for a variety of pH values. One word of caution—one noted aquarist says that stabilizing the pH at 8.3 will make fish more susceptible to ammonia poisoning and suggests that a thin layer of gravel from a conditioned aquarium be added to the transport bag to reduce ammonia buildup in transit.

7

OBSERVING BEHAVIOR

 s fascinating as the surroundings in which an animal finds itself is the study of how it behaves in that environment. You can investigate this either in a natural setting or by keeping the animal in an aquarium.

Keep in mind that the aquarium is an artificial domain and that some stimuli present in nature will be absent in that necessarily limited milieu. Therefore, some of an animal's responses will be missing from its repertoire or at least significantly modified. If one can extrapolate from the behavior of caged creatures, a common result of captivity is a loss of excitability.

Remember that the aquarium may present the animal with heretofore unknown stimuli that it has never dealt with in nature and it may respond abnormally as a consequence. Even a known stimulus may present itself in such a way that the animal cannot effectively deal with it. Consider an animal confined with another that represents a mortal threat. Its response will probably be of little avail in such a confined space where there is nowhere to run. If the cue to such a threat is chemical, an exudate emanating from its enemy, the water will soon become saturated with it, continually impinging upon the hapless animal without offering guidance as to what direction the threat lies in.

Observing behavior requires active patience. You must absorb what the animal does and think about it while enduring long periods in which the animal does little or nothing. If during such periods you are basically asleep with your eyes open, you will miss nuances such as intent moves that predict what the animal will do next that are important components of its basic character.

Some animals' actions are so slow that compressing time via time-lapse video offers the only reasonable way to watch the result of their ponderous and time-consuming movements. Time-lapse technique involves setting up a video such that only a few frames of tape will be exposed at each of a series of regularly spaced intervals. When played back at normal speed, the time over which movements take place is greatly compressed.

An initial problem among animal watchers is an over-active imagination coupled with anthropomorphism; that is, reading more into an animal's response than the evidence warrants and putting that response into human terms, usually by granting the animal more powers of reason than it possesses.

The easiest way to solve this tendency is to read the works of well-known behaviorists who have studied specific groups of animals. Few have dealt with marine species; most have concentrated on social insects, such as ants, bees, birds, or higher vertebrates. Texts on behavior, ethology, or sociobiology will mention marine as well as terrestial studies in which the investigator was able to uncover and make sense of a hitherto unknown behavior pattern.

As an aid to developing your powers of observation, keep a small creature in your aquarium whose life style has been thoroughly studied and for which you can get that information. The stickleback, a small fish, is one example. Using the information as a guide, watch its behavior over a long period of time and see if you reach the same conclusions as the investigator. Keep in mind that aside from eating, resting, and exploring, the most vivid displays may emerge only upon sexual maturity when attracting a mate, building a nest, and guarding a territory manifest themselves.

Not all behavioral topics are equally accessible to the marine naturalist. You can listen to the sounds of whales or the echolocation clicks of porpoises in the sea, but you probably do not have the means to stay at sea very long and correlate those sounds with other behavior. The same can be said of migration. Many of these animals cover thousands of miles in the course of the seasons. Tracking those wanderings must be left to the professional who has the use of satellite telemetry, radio transmitters, and the like.

You also have other limitations. You can observe the mating behavior of a crab or the aggressive postures of a territorial fish, but you are unlikely to have the means to correlate this with hormonal or other physiological changes in the animal that may accompany these events.

Don't despair. There is still much to be found by straightforward observation that may or may not require coupling with a few simple experiments. A recent report in *Science* underlines the fact that simple observation and a simple experiment can still uncover a fundamentally important idea.

A scientist noted that the males of a species of small, tropical fish called a green swordtail attract females in proportion to the length of its bright, sword-like appendage which seems to serve no other useful purpose. The swordtails have a close relative, the platyfish, in which the males have no sword-like appendage at all. When an artificial tail was added to the male platyfish, he was much more attractive to the female platyfish. Both the platyfish and the swordtail belong to the same genus. Biologists believe the platyfish is geologically older than the swordtail.

What this experiment infers is that the female platyfish has a latent, innate tendency awaiting an external cue such as that which developed in male swordtails. Thus the female platyfish has responded to a visual stimulus before it has come into being through evolution. The experiment suggests that should a male platyfish develop a bright appendage by mutation, that mutation would be eminently successful.

The evolutionary implications of these results are still a matter of debate. Most workers in this field believe that structure precedes behavior. Here is an instance where it might be the other way around. Scientists have also felt that male attractants are always coupled with some advantage to the species; strength, resistance to disease, large size, etc., but this experiment shows an attractant that has no coupling at all with survival value.

An animal's behavior is as critical to its existence as is its structure. It must use what it has been given as effectively as it can to find food, shelter, a mate, avoid predators, and cope with other threats.

Its behavior can be almost entirely endowed or learned, adjusting to new situations either by trial-and-error or by witnessing the responses of others.

The difference between a "lower" and "higher" animal, where we take it as gospel that a learned response is of a higher order than an innate reaction, is often a matter of degree rather than kind. Granted that very simple animals can do little more than react either to internal or external stimuli and have very little with which to respond, while more complex animals have a wider range of options, all animals, including humans, are endowed to some extent.

That endowment is, for the most part, useful, and has allowed the particular species to endure; it is part and parcel of its phylogenetic inheritance. That is to say, it's innate behavior is as much a species distinction as it's morphology, an inheritance from its evolutionary past.

Remember, though, that a species may also carry useless baggage; evolutionary remnants that no longer serve a current purpose, as with the appendix in man, or useless behavioral leftovers.

Even among lower forms, animals may possess an elaborate repertoire which is ready to perform on demand from birth. However, some behavior patterns do not manifest themselves immediately and can only be evoked with maturation.

The distinction between what is endowed and what is learned is often unclear. Instinctive behavior may almost immediately be modified by responses to the environment that either reinforce the specific action or squelch it.

Lower animals appear to have less ability to add to their repertoire by experience. Higher animals often have a protracted period of adolescence which provides the opportunity to learn while lower animals are thrown into the breach of survival almost immediately and need the means to fend for themselves from early on.

SOME SPECIFIC BEHAVIOR PATTERNS

Only a few examples of specific behavior patterns can be given here. Much more exists in the literature, everything from the chemical responses of the amoeba to the nurturing behavior of the bottle-nosed dolphin.

An animal's range of response patterns depends on it's structure, sensory organs, organs of locomotion, and integrative circuitry. To capture food, a sponge can do little more than beat the water with its flagella to provide a current that will flow through its canals, hopefully carrying nourishment with it to be taken up by its flagellated collar cells. It's means of defense is passive—it manufactures and distributes toxins throughout its body which make it completely unpalatable to all but a few predators.

A cnidarian can do more. A jellyfish or anemone can move and put tentacles loaded with stinging nematocysts to good use for catching food. If a tentacle is brushed mechanically, just a few nematocysts will fire; if that is coupled with a protein discharge from its victim, a whole battery of nematocysts will let go and the tentacles will close in, bringing more sting cells to bear. The tentacles are coordinated by a simple nerve net which will direct the movement of food into its mouth where it is digested.

This kind of behavior has been called a stimulus-response reaction and implies that the animal does nothing unless an internal or external stimulus is applied. But anemones, as quiet as they seem to be, do make longitudinal movements when to all appearances, nothing is happening. (Proving nothing is happening is an impossible task; you can always counter that the stimulation is there but it isn't easily perceived.)

In jellyfish the medusa continually pulses, a rhythmical contraction controlled by an internal mechanism. As one observer put it, they "continually listen to their own bell."

Corals exemplify a common characteristic among animals—they fight when confronted by "foreign" tissue. Corals are composed of individual yet connected zooids basically constructed much like anemones. Corals of different species will grow very close to one another in competition for space. As they come into contact, the bordering zooids of each species will attack one another. One of the two colonies may overcome the other or it may result in a standoff where neither encroaches any further. Their relative aggressiveness was determined by experiment in the laboratory but has not proved to be predictable in the field.

Much of the rhythm of life in the sea is directly or indirectly influenced by the daily and monthly excursions of the sun and moon. Activity cycles of intertidal animals are determined by the tides. For example, fiddler crabs remain quietly in their burrows during high tide and come out to feed during low tide. If you put a fiddler crab in a damp, dark box it will continue to follow those tidal cycles; that is active for six plus hours then quiescent for the next six and so on, for up to a month.

Light also controls the activities of many animals. The vertical migration of plankton in the sea is a good example. The precision with which the mating behavior of certain polychaete worms is controlled by light is nothing short of extraordinary. The Atlantic palolo worm only breeds during a few nights in July and only during the third lunar quarter. Swarms of just the posterior halves of the worm (called epitokes) migrate to the surface and discharge eggs and sperm while the anterior end of the worm remains burrowed in the bottom. Even more exact are the requirements for the Bermuda fireworm. It breeds during most months of the year, but mainly in the summer months. Breeding peaks on the third night after a full moon for about three minutes, exactly fifty-six minutes after sunset. Males and females swarm to the surface where the females discharge their eggs in a bioluminescent cloud. The males rush into the cloud discharging sperm accompanied by bright, luminescent flashes of light.

Swarming for sexual purposes occurs among many species. The male polychaete, *Nereis succina,* swims in circles around the female and discharges sperm. In response, the female sheds her eggs. The circling dance of the male is triggered by a chemical stimulant from the female.

The common American squid and the Pacific Coast squid swim in schools of as few as ten to many thousands. When it comes time to breed they do so en masse. After fertilization, the females seek the bottom and lay eggs that are encased in cigar-sized sacs containing over fifty embryos each. They attach the sacs together in community clusters that have the appearance of the business end of an oversized dustmop. The eggs rapidly develop and hatch without any parental aid. The common octopus, on the other hand, lays its eggs alone in an enclosed lair and continuously circulates water over them until they hatch.

Parenthood in fish ranges from complete indifference, as in schooling fish who do little more than simultaneously discharge sperm and eggs into the sea, then move on, to those that prepare a nest, go through a courtship ritual, then guard the eggs until they have hatched. A few species go further and protect their offspring until they are capable of feeding on their own.

Courtship display also takes place among the more mobile invertebrates. Male fiddler crabs dig a burrow, then wave their large claws in specific patterns to attract a female. The details of this beckoning varies among species and enables the female to recognize a male of their own species on a beach where two or more other species of fiddler crabs may intermingle. A male *Uca pugnax* further confirms the claw signal by bowing once or twice in front of the female. On the other hand, *Uca rapax* doesn't bow at all. *Uca beebei* males turn around in front of females while *Uca stenodactyla* runs to and fro in front of the female.

Much of this kind of behavior is entirely innate, unlearned, and pro-

FIDDLER CRABS

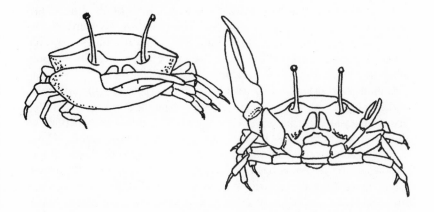

Studying behavior takes concentrated observation. Male fiddler crabs signal for prospective mates with claw movements that are distinctive for their species and that allow rapid pairing up on a flat that contains several species.

grammed into the genotype. That is not to say that an animal is incapable of adaptive behavior. It is, but the presence of a specific stimulus automatically sets off a preordained response that is present from the time it is born.

Konrad Lorenz, an ethologist, calls this behavior a "species-characteristic drive-action" (The German *arteigene triebhandlung* doesn't translate into anything more succinct.) It is a set of neurophysiological sequences in which a selective response to a specific stimulus releases a fixed motor pattern. Put another way, a pattern of movements is evoked by an impulse internally produced but held in check until externally released by what has come to be called an "innate releasing mechanism," or IRM.

This pattern of movement and its trigger, the IRM, is as constant within a species as its common physical characteristics. These motor sequences have a phylogenetic origin and are part and parcel of the animal's inheritance. As such, they are highly resistant to individual modification. All animals, however, have a feedback circuit that interprets the consequences of their behavior, specifically whether it is useful or not under prevailing circumstances.

Probably in no other species of marine aquatic animal is this mode of behavior as easy to study as the hermit crab. Because they are ceaselessly active, hermits make good aquarium additions. They are easy to maintain. Feed them brine shrimp and an occasional bit of seaweed. Forget hunks of meat that might entice other crabs; hermits eat only small fragments and will not tear big pieces apart.

Unlike other critters of the order Decapoda (prawns, shrimp, crabs, and lobsters), hermit crabs do not come equipped with a full suit of armor. They lack any hard parts aft of their cephalothorax, which leaves their soft and defenseless hindquarters exposed to easy assault.

Their evolutionary response to nature providing only plated gloves and jacket but no pants has been to employ empty snail shells as leggings. Since hermits of various species come in different sizes, each must habituate the haunts of a similarly sized snail host to find a custom fit. In the shallow waters of mid-Atlantic shores, *Pagurus longicarpus,* the most common of the small tideline hermits, inhabits the shells of the periwinkle, the mud snail, and the little moon snail. Their larger cousin, *P. pollicaris,* abundant in deeper waters from Maine to Florida, suit themselves in the carbonate remains of the whelks, the sand collar snail, and moon snails or any other large shell it can find.

On the west coast, the tidepool hermits, *P. sameulis* and *P. granosimanus,* have an overwhelming fondness for *Tegula* shells whereas *P. hirsutiusculus,* more plentiful in deeper water, prefer *Acanthina* or *Olivella.*

Aside from the daily grind of searching for food and occasional sexual forays, the hermit finds house hunting a consuming preoccupation, a task of which it never tires. Presented with a cluster of empty shells, the hermit ritually repeats an elaborate inspection of each one, turning the shell over and over, probing its passages, and if eminently suitable, popping out of its old home into its new one. Even a new shell does not stop it from going through the same routine with every new encounter. If it comes across a shell it has recently examined, the normal rigamarole will be duly abbreviated as it somehow senses it is going over ancient history.

If a new shell is already occupied by a hermit, another hermit crab is not deterred from the shell game. If the bigger of the two decides it wants to try out the shell of its smaller acquaintance, it is sure to get its way. The vanquished, forced to withdraw from the shell, is not molested by the victor and will usually pop into the victor's hand-me-down or, if that's not possible, quickly burrow into the sand to get out of harm's way before some other predator comes along to take a snap at its hind-quarters.

This behavior offers you a chance to experiment and discover how or if changed circumstances will modify it. Thus, if you were to partly fill some empty shells with plaster of Paris or, more challenging, lightweight, plastic foam, will the hermit learn by examination that the shells are useless as a new home?

To what extent can the hermit be taught? Can the hermit recognize the utility of a shell by its color or its species? If you introduce two species of shells, morphologically different but within the size range the hermit can use, spoiling one species but not the other, what will be the hermit's response? If you introduce objects that are unlike a snail but contain an orifice, what will the hermit do? How curved, how light, or how hard does an object have to be before the hermit becomes interested? Set up an aquarium and try and find out.

As curious as patterns of responses of individual animals are, the behavior of conspecifics, that is, groups of the same species, hold even more mysteries. The initial question to ask yourself about group behavior is, "Is what I observe simply a collection of individual responses or truly a group response?" Many invertebrates swarm toward light as individuals, yet the collective result looks like a group response. Fish milling about are a collection of individuals, but a school of fish swimming in close proximity to one another, all aligned in the same direction and aware of the slightest change in speed and direction of the group, behaves as a unit and becomes something of a superorganism.

There are plenty of instances where it is difficult to tell whether responses are collective or individual. For example, a tropic reef is a haven for many species of small fish who will flee into its nooks and crannies at the first sign of trouble. When all is well they hover over the reef looking for tidbits passing by in the currents. Collectively they fall inside a hemisphere beyond which none of their members stray. As a predator approaches, the volume of the hemisphere begins to shrink.

Should the predator charge the reef, the hemisphere collapses into the reef with incredible speed and uniformity. Is this a collective response or simply a group of individual responses? Much the same could be asked of the converse actions of a small school of fish isolated in open water and faced by a predator. At first they tighten, forming as small a ball as they can. If the predator darts in to their center they explode outward uniformly in all directions much like an aerial star shell.

Intraspecific associations among sea life seem more widespread than among land creatures. Sea creatures often share food and quarters. In many symbiotic relationships there isn't a great deal that the host can do about the presence of the guest, but in others, either appears to have the right to call it quits if they so chose. The nature of these arrangements, that is, what brings them together and what ties them to one another, is simply not understood.

USING TECHNOLOGY TO STUDY BEHAVIOR

If you have the technical know-how and the knack to plan, design, and build mechanical and electronic contrivances, there are a number of avenues of exploration open to you, such as the time-lapse video suggested earlier.

To rig a video camera to record time-lapse sequences requires that the camera be firmly mounted, that the shutter can be tripped one frame at a time by a solenoid or electrical pulse, and that the pulse or solenoid be controlled by a timer that will repeatedly trigger it at constant intervals. Those intervals should be adjustable so that you can change the apparent rate of time compression. You might also construct the unit such that the timing mechanism turns a light on during exposure and off again after the exposure cycle is complete.

Units have also been devised to go underwater in natural settings. To attempt anything this complex—a completely watertight battery operated camera, lights, and intervalometer—requires access to a small machine shop and the skill to use it.

In an earlier chapter, the basic requirements for recording underwater sounds were outlined. Animals produce sound over a wide range of frequencies, some so low that, for humans, they are more felt than heard, while others produce ultrasounds pitched well above the response of the human ear.

Animals can not only modulate sound frequency, they can vary volume and the temporal spacing of the sounds. Once these sounds are recorded they can be read out through an oscillograph to yield a graphical record called a sound spectrogram or sonagram. Doing this at modest cost requires the application of the art of the electronic tinkerer who can adapt a piece of surplus equipment to the task.

The kinds of senses of marine animals go beyond sight, hearing, smell, taste, or touch. Recording the information a fish receives, for example, can be a formidable task even for the marine naturalist with a flair for electronics. Fish respond to extremely low vibrations through their lateral line system. Some, including sharks, respond to the miniscule electrical currents produced by muscle activity of their prey. Others are said to respond to the earth's magnetic field. An intrepid investigator who can apply detection methods from some other scientific discipline may find whole new subject areas for exploration.

8

PLANKTON

The drifting life in the sea is collectively called plankton. The word comes from the Greek meaning for wanderer and is applied to all marine forms that go where the currents carry them. Some can swim (making remarkable daily vertical excursions), but none approach the capabilities of fish to go as they choose.

Plankton are not evenly distributed throughout the sea. Coastal waters rich in nutrients, support large populations during some seasons, but warm mid-ocean waters do not. The upper latitude coastal waters of North America abound with plankton for all but a short time in mid-winter.

The plankton come in a bewildering number of forms over a wide size range. A chain of salps can be over thirty feet long and a northern jellyfish can trail tentacles nearly sixty feet. Yet the bulk of the plankton are just on the edge of visibility or below it and require a microscope to see them and identify them—a panorama of life that extends from the yellow and blue-green algae that make up the bulk of the phytoplankton to an array of zooplankton that contain representatives of every major phylum in the animal kingdom, including some found nowhere but in the sea. Still smaller forms abound that go right through tow nets and must be collected with equipment too expensive for the amateur naturalist.

Some plankton spend all their lives adrift, others only a part of their existence. The latter are mainly juvenile and larval forms of animals that either develop into swimmers or settle out to live on or in the bottom—swimmers like shrimp or fish, sessile animals like sponges or hydrozoans, crawlers like crabs or prawns, and burrowers like polychaete worms or clams. These tiny offspring look nothing like their parents and identifying them presents quite a challenge.

Many of the smallest plankton are algae, plant-like creatures that synthesize their food using sunlight and dissolved carbon dioxide. These are collectively called phytoplankton. (Animal plankters are collectively called zooplankton.) The phytoplankton are the foundation of the sea's food chain. They are fed upon by small zooplankton who in turn are fed upon by larger zooplankters, sessile invertebrates, fish, and baleen whales.

The most numerous animal species on earth is a copepod, a crustacean only a few millimeters in length, *Calanus finmarchicus*. It (and like copepods) are the main food supply for the teeming billions of small fish like herrings, anchovies, pilchards, mackerel, and others upon whom many other species of fish depend for their survival.

An interest in plankton can become a lifetime pursuit. Every animal phylum in the sea has representatives in the plankton. With most of the planktonic species their life cycles are not well understood nor is their distribution or habits.

COLLECTING PLANKTON

Simply by looking into the water with a face mask you can see dozens of the larger species, although it is unlikely you will see all of them during the same season. You can retrieve the larger forms with a bucket or dip-net—jellyfish, comb-jellies, salps, and more—although a plastic kitchen sieve or colander will do better; either is gentler on fragile species. Take care to avoid the tentacles of stinging jellyfish; they can pack a surprising wallop. If you do get stung, remove the tentacles, then treat the affected area with ammonia, baking soda, or meat tenderizer.

Avoid overcrowding collecting jars if you intend to keep your specimens alive. Most specimens will succumb within a day or so unless carefully tended. Even so, some species die rapidly despite the care you take, and their demise quickly affects the remaining creatures in the jar.

Don't put these animals into your main aquarium. Watch them in a small aquarium. Most of them will not last for more than a few days even if provided with aeration and some form of vertical agitation.

The bulk of plankton are small and can barely be seen with the naked eye. A great many others can only be seen with a microscope. Often they are very thinly dispersed in the sea. To gather and concentrate them, a fine-meshed net is towed through the water at a slow speed.

A plankton net is made of woven nylon with uniform openings. Coarse weaves—thirty-five meshes to the inch—are used to collect zooplankton, and finer weaves—150 meshes per inch—are used for phytoplankton. Still smaller creatures can be filtered out—this is done with very fine filter material mounted on fritted glass with a vacuum applied to the underside.

The net is a long, narrow cone: the larger end is held open by a frame attached to a tow rope via a three- or four-line bridle connected to a swivel. A wide-mouthed bottle is attached at the narrow end. You can buy the net and frame through a biological supply house or you can make something that will do for a few tows from a nylon stocking (see diagram). A wooden or plastic embroidery hoop can also be used for the wide end.

To gather plankton, pull the net through the water no faster than two to three knots. At slow speeds the water passes through the net leaving the plankton trapped on the meshes. At higher speeds, the water is simply pushed ahead of the net and its filtering efficiency drops dramatically. In some seasons, a five-minute tow will fill the collecting bottle. Other times life is sparse and longer tows are necessary.

You can still collect plankton if you do not have a boat. River and tidal flow are sufficiently fast to do the filtering for you. Simply find a pier or culvert and wait for the appropriate tide. If the water is shallow, a float just in front of the net will prevent it from sinking and getting torn on the bottom. If the water is deep, you might want to add a weight (an old sashweight works well) to depress the net below the surface. Different species of plankton may occupy different depths during the day, and weighing the net is the only way of collecting them.

Collecting at sunrise and just after sunset will yield species not seen during midday. Certain animal plankton are repelled by the light and sink down in the water column during daylight, then rise again as the light diminishes. These diurnal migrations are astounding feats considering the animals' sizes and the distances covered. This migration has many mysteries; many phyla do it, yet its survival value is not obvious and its purpose is still a matter of speculation.

At night you can concentrate certain species, copepods and others, by shining a strong beam over the side and dip-netting those that are

HOMEMADE PLANKTON NET

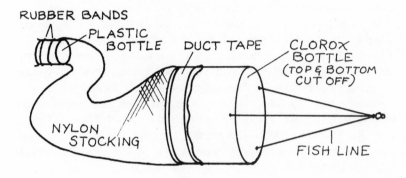

RUBBER BANDS

PLASTIC BOTTLE

DUCT TAPE

CLOROX BOTTLE (TOP & BOTTOM CUT OFF)

NYLON STOCKING

FISH LINE

attracted to the light. Your light will also attract fish, squid, shrimp, and a host of other predators.

OBSERVING PLANKTON

Under a low-power microscope, planktonic life dashes, swims, and wriggles from one side of the specimen dish to the other in bursting profusion. You may have as many as fifty species in one tow; some that move slowly and others that dart in and out of your field of view before you can get a good look at them. You can slow down the fast ones by adding an anesthetic—seltzer (the carbon dioxide does it), epsom salts (magnesium ions slow the nerve impulses of many invertebrates), or toothache drops (benzocaine is the active ingredient). To find out what works best, experiment. Biological supply houses also supply additives that will raise the viscosity of the water, making it much tougher for the animal to swim through it.

If you cannot view the material immediately upon returning home, you can extend their lives by aerating their environment and cooling them either in an ice chest or a refrigerator, but not too cold, or they will die of thermal shock.

PRESERVING PLANKTON

If you decide to permanently preserve your catch, add Formalin to the specimen jar—one part Formalin (a 37% formaldehyde solution) to twenty-five parts seawater. Some fragile forms will distort badly and should be anesthetized before Formalin treatment. Check its effects on a portion of the sample. Be careful with Formalin—it irritates the eyes and is poisonous. Flush spills with copious amounts of water. If you get it in your eyes, rinse them thoroughly and get to a doctor.

Because Formalin fumes are so irritating, many prefer to work with a weaker solution; about 10% by volume. To obtain this, mix 27 ml of Formalin (37%) to 100 ml of seawater. Formalin solutions turn acidic over time and will disintegrate specimens stored in it. Add a pinch of borax or baking soda for better long-term storage.

Because formaldehyde has been associated with cancer in lab animals, some biologists now preserve everything in alcohol. Ethyl alcohol is preferable to others. If you cannot find denatured ethyl alcohol (usually obtained from a hardware store) then use high-proof vodka or neutral spirits from a liquor store.

Don't use Formalin for preserving algae—use Lugol's solution. To make it, dissolve one gram of iodine in a solution of two grams of potassium iodide in 100 ml of water. Add enough Lugol's solution to the sample to give it a distinctly orange color. If you can't get the ingredients for Lugol's solution, use tincture of iodine. Remember to label what you collect with date, location, and diary reference.

MAGNIFICATION

A low-power binocular microscope will cover the 10X to 30X magnification range. Above that you will need a compound microscope which usually has combinations of magnifications from 20X to 1,000X. Above 100X, however, you will have to expend time and effort preparing the specimens for high magnification and learn how to get the most out of the instrument under high magnifications.

If your magnification capabilities are limited to a hand lens or a low-power binocular microscope, your main interest will necessarily be confined to the larger zooplankton, many of which are large enough to see with simple equipment.

ZOOPLANKTON

Every major animal phylum has a member in the plankton, either as an adult or in a larval stage. Those that spend their whole lives adrift are called holoplankton, those who spend just a part of it, meroplankton. Meroplankton include both larval forms like fish eggs as well as mature forms that have drifting as well as sessile stages.

To go over all the forms of animals in the plankton requires a reiteration of the animal phyla and their classes, a task already well done in a number of easily available textbooks. What we can do here briefly is mention what is easy to find in the plankton and where you might look for representatives not so easy to spot or to identify once you have found them.

PROTOZOA

Now in their own kingdom but once grouped with the animals, you will see a major class in the plankton, the Sarcodina, that contains two orders you could spend the rest of your life investigating: the Foraminifera and the Radiolaria.

Radiolarians are exclusively marine. Their latticed silica structure usually has a central capsule which radiates intricate spicules. Their remains settle to the bottom forming a characteristic ooze in modern seas; beds of chert are the result of such settling in Tertiary times.

The shells of Foraminifera, or forams, also create characteristic layers on the bottom of the sea. Most of the marine forms have calcareous shells. *Globigerina* is the most prolific of them.

SPONGES

The sponges are a side branch of the evolutionary tree. Their larva are planktonic but seldom seen in net hauls. The gemmules, as the asexual larva are called, can be obtained directly from the source. In July or August, collect some of the encrusting brown sponges (*Mycale* sp.) found on wharf pilings. Plunk it into a jar of sea water; keep it cool, but don't aerate it. You should have some free swimmers within hours.

Don't wait too long to examine them; they settle down to the quiet life within days.

CNIDARIA (FORMERLY COELENTERATA)

The Cnidaria are a large, ancient phylum that will be represented in most of your summer tows. They vary widely in size from jellyfish only a few millimeters in diameter to large jellyfish seen in cold waters as well as warm. Large jellyfish, such as *Cyanea,* often have small groups of fish swimming beneath them. In the warm Gulf Stream waters, many exotic species exist that have no common names; *Diphyopsis, Physophora, Cupulita,* as well as one you know, *Physalia,* the Portuguese man-of-war. These are best seen in the water but be careful—wear a long-sleeved shirt and long pants. The sight of a *Physalia* or *Chrysaora,* the sea nettle, is not sufficient compensation for the sting they can deliver if you are careless enough to blunder into one.

CTENOPHORA

Jellyfish-like and for many years classified with them, the comb-jellies are a separate phylum. Their population can explode in summertime in northern waters and you will find your net clogged with them. Common are *Beroe, Mnemiopsis,* and the smaller *Pleurobrachia* whose comb-plates flash like diamonds in sunlit water.

Ctenophores will keep for a few days in cool, aerated, seawater. Also, they are phosphorescent—you can make them flash in the dark by gently disturbing them mechanically.

ARTHROPODA

The dominant animals in most of your catches will be arthropods, primarily members of the class Crustacea. This is a large and complicated group and you will have to flesh out the following quick description for yourself.

The class is subdivided into seven subclasses. Certain orders and suborders of four of these subclasses make up the majority of the forms you can easily identify.

The subclass Branchipoda contains the suborder Cladocera. Cladocerans, especially *Evadne* and *Podon* are common.

The Copepoda are both abundant and diverse. The most well known is *Calanus,* but other commonly seen genera include *Arcatia, Centro-*

pages, Corycarus, Paracalanus, and *Pseudocalanus.* Only a dedicated plankton picker can sort out the differences among species with speed and accuracy.

The Cirripedia include the acorn barnacle. Its free-swimming nauplii larva turn up regularly.

The Malacostraca contain the higher crustaceans—shrimps, crayfish, lobster, and crabs. The larval and smaller stages of the larger forms are a study in themselves and delightful to watch develop. Many will keep well in small aquariums.

LARVAL FORMS

Adults of many other phyla are in the plankton, but the larval form of just about every creature that is widely dispersed abounds in the plankton. Summer tows will supply you with mollusks, ectoprocts, echinoderms, protochordates, urochordates, and chordates, all in bewildering profusion. The eggs and fry of common fish are often found but not easy to identify.

ODD OTHERS

The arrow worms, Chaetognatha, are represented by *Saggita* sp. which has a pre-fish appearance; slender with narrow, symmetrical fins and a head with a set of recurved spines that can close like ice tongs.

The Urochordata are entirely marine. These include the salps—transparent, ribboned, barrel-shaped creatures that occur either singly or in long aggregates and range from a few tenths of an inch in length to six inches or better.

PHYTOPLANKTON

Unlike those on land, most photosynthesizers in the sea are one-celled algae, which occur singly or in colonies. The important ones are diatoms, encased in intricate, latticed boxes of silica; the flagellates, motile creatures in cellulose enclosures, and coccolithophores, extremely small forms covered with plates of calcium carbonate. Coccolithophores and other extremely small forms are collectively called nannoplankton.

All algae cells contain pigment bodies called chloroplasts that manufacture carbohydrates from dissolved carbon dioxide and nutrients when the sun shines on them. The algae are primary producers upon which most of the animal life in the sea depends.

DIATOMS

A high percentage of the plant-like life of the ocean are diatoms—algae that encase themselves in elaborate silica structures. Their outer structure is usually the main means of identifying them. These skeletons are quite beautiful, but so intricate that you will need a good quality compound microscope to appreciate them. In times past they were used by microscopists for testing lenses, so fine is their detail.

You can view many of them directly while alive, or if they are abundant enough in your sample and you can concentrate enough of them for manipulation, you can chemically clean them to remove tissues that might otherwise obscure their structures.

The classic way to do this is boil them in nitric acid which will destroy all organic matter in the sample. Its fumes, however, are noxious, it will burn your skin, and it is now hard to obtain unless you have access to a chemist's laboratory. A less effective substitute is Clorox, which should be heated. After boiling, let the diatoms settle to the bottom of the vessel (usually a test tube) and decant the liquid. Pour in water, let them settle again; repeat this washing process several times. Then spread the sediment on a glass microscope slide and let them dry. Make a permanent mount by adding a drop or two of the highest refractive index mounting media you have, add a cover glass, and store the slide flat.

DINOFLAGELLATES

Dinoflagellates are motile, can feed on solid or dissolved matter and can manufacture nutrients using sunlight. Some of its members are phosphorescent. Noctiluca is one such, common in summer, and an added joy to a night at sea. Pull your hand through the water and watch the myriad tiny, sparkling lights.

The dinoflagellates are well known for their sudden and enormous reproductive surges, their very numbers discoloring the water over considerable areas. If they are green or blue, you will scarcely notice it, but if they're red, the adjacent locale will speak of red tide which often means shellfish beds will be closed. Some species ingested by intermediates (shellfish) that are then eaten by man, cause paralytic shellfish poisoning.

9

MARINE BACTERIA

lthough definitions of marine microbiology can be as inclusive as all organisms in the sea that are uni-cellular—including certain fungi, yeasts, algae, and protozoans—our limit here is to bacteria.

Bacteria in the sea play a major role in the conversion of both simple and complex matter: they break down complex, organic matter, assimilate carbon dioxide without photosynthesis, oxidize and reduce nitrogen compounds, fix nitrogen, and reduce and oxidize sulfur compounds, as well as a host of other conversions.

What most people know about bacteria relates to the parasitic nature of some species to humans; that is, as causative agents of disease. Although disease-producing bacteria can be present in seawater through pollution, marine bacteria rarely affect humans; in fact, saltwater has a bactericidal effect on most known (but not all) human pathogens.

If you perform your investigations of marine bacteria using the same precautions as you would to prevent infections from any source, and additionally sterilize any cultures of bacteria you may grow before disposing of them, you have less to fear than when performing the same kinds of investigations on soil bacteria. In fact, many of the techniques used in medicine for determining pathogenic species, such as the use of sera and agglutinins, are not pertinent to bacteria from the sea.

CLASSIFYING MARINE BACTERIA

Because marine bacteria are so adaptable to their surroundings and can vary in form and biochemical character when kept on artificial media, the problems of identifying them can be considerable.

Bacteria take several basic forms—spheres (cocci), rods (straight or curved) or spirals. They can be motile or not, and some can form heat-resistant spores which can appear as bumps either on the end or middle of the rods. Some bacteria grow well in air (aerobes), in the absence of air (anaerobes) or both (facultative anaerobes). Many marine bacteria are autotrophic; that is, they synthesize their own food from very basic compounds. Among these are rods that use hydrogen sulfide anaerobically, aerobically oxidize nitrogen compounds (as in a saltwater aquarium), aerobically oxidize methane, or aerobically oxidize sulfides or sulfur (the last are especially plentiful in estuarine muds).

The most common marine bacteria are rod-shaped heterotrophs, those that break down detritus and other organic matter. Fortunately, many of these can be told apart by their shape, motility, and the appearance of their colonies which may be pigmented as well as differentiated by shape, surface texture, and edge appearance.

COLLECTING BACTERIA

You can collect bacteria directly from the water column, from detritus (such as the stones from your aquarium) or from silt and mud. As you collect, do so as aseptically as possible; that is, use clean, sterile transferring devices and containers so that you avoid stray contaminants by terrestrial and airborne bacteria.

To collect marine bacteria from mud bottoms, use a corer with rubber stoppers to fit each end. Rinse the tube and stoppers in dilute Clorox to minimize contamination before use. Keep the tube stoppered until just before use.

To use, remove the stoppers and shove the tube down into the mud. Remove the tube and replace the stoppers. Wash off the outside of the tube. If you cannot use the tube contents for a day or so, put the whole tube intact in the refrigerator. To sample the mud, push it out of the tube with a large diameter dowel. Cut the cylinder of mud with a sterile knife (heat the blade in a flame or dip it in dilute Clorox). Pick out representative pieces of mud with a sterile spoon and mix with sterile seawater, roughly one ml of sediment to two mls of seawater. Take one ml of this and dilute to ten ml in sterile seawater. Repeat the dilution again. This technique is called serial dilution. Place a small sample of the diluted solution into test tubes containing growth media. The idea is to dilute the thousands of bacteria in the original sample down to a low enough number so that when each bacterium multiplies on the medium it will form a single, distinct, easily seen colony. You will then have few enough colonies that you can count them; they will be far enough apart on the medium to isolate for further identification; and you can determine the physical characteristics of the colony.

STERILE TECHNIQUES

You will need sterile tools, seawater, and culture media. Anything that can be fitted into a pressure cooker and heated to fifteen pounds pressure for twenty minutes will emerge sterile. Culture media must be sterilized immediately after it has been mixed.

After making up the media (but before sterilization) pour about two ml of liquid media into each of as many six-inch glass test tubes as you can muster. Plug each tube with a cotton wad. Stick the test tubes into a wide mouth jar to hold them upright. Put the excess media into a narrow mouth bottle that can be sealed with a plastic cap. Don't close the cap tight. Fit all of this into a pressure cooker and sterilize the lot. Also sterilize a few medicine droppers.

When you open the pressure cooker, shut the lid tight on the bottle containing the media and store it in the refrigerator for future use. As the media in the test tubes cools, it will set. If you roll the tubes at an acute angle you will coat the walls with media before it sets and thus increase the usable surface area in the tube. You may also use Petri dishes for this media, but they are not as easy to come by as test tubes.

For transferring things to and from the sterile test tubes you will have to "flame" the mouth of the tube after every withdrawal of the cotton plug. Don't set the plug down or touch the part of the plug that enters the test tube. Learn to pull out the plug between your third and fourth index finger and use your thumb and forefinger to hold the tube. Always flame any surface before inserting it in the tube and the mouth of the tube itself to kill any airborne bacteria that may cling to the glass or metal insert.

After you are finished with tools or cultures, sterilize all equipment before washing it and making it ready for further work. Marine bacteria are not dangerous to humans but a few human disease bacteria are known to be viable in salt water.

CULTURE MEDIA

Autotrophic bacteria can grow in very simple media. For example, the nitrogen bacteria lining the bottom stones of your aquarium need noth-

MARINE BACTERIA

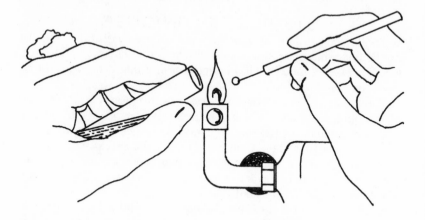

The rim of the test tube must be flame sterilized every time the tube is unplugged or it will become contaminated with unwanted bacteria.

ing more than aerated seawater that has traces of fish urine and fecal matter in it.

Heterotrophic bacteria need a media with protein in it as well as sea salts. The media must be made up with seawater, for many marine bacteria will not grow without it. If you cannot get clean seawater, use:

potassium chloride	0.75 gm
magnesium sulfate (Epsom salts)	7.0 gm
sodium chloride (Kosher salt)	23.4 gm
water to	1.00 liter

This formula is equivalent to a seawater salinity of thirty-one parts per thousand (ppt). If you are investigating bacteria in an estuary, determine the salinity of the local water and add enough water to this formula to cut the salinity to whatever prevails locally, usually twelve-to-twenty ppt.

For culture media, get agar from a biological supply house and make up the following formula:

Agar	7 gm
Beef bouillon cube	1 gm
Powdered egg	3 gm
Seawater (about 25 ppt.)	to 250 ml

Or, if you can get the ingredients, here is a second recipe:

Peptone	5 gm
Ferric phosphate	0.1 gm
Agar	15 gm
Seawater	1,000 ml

Heat the seawater to dissolve the agar, then add the rest of the ingredients.

INOCULATING CULTURE TUBES

Bacteria can be transferred into culture tubes with a wire loop or by pipette. For example, with the mud sample, add the diluted mud infusion to the tube, replug the tube (remember to flame the mouth again) and swirl the liquid around to wet the entire media surface. Let the tubes sit at 75°F for four to eight days, then examine and count the colonies formed. By quantifying the dilutions and additions you can estimate the numbers of live bacteria in the original sample.

Examine the colonies carefully. Are they all alike in color, shape, and structure? If not, that signifies they are different species.

VIEWING BACTERIA

To mount the bacteria on microscope slides, affix a piece of thin, iron wire (or nichrome wire, if you can get it) to the end of a ¼-inch diameter by 6-inch dowel and bend the free end into a small loop. To sterilize the end of the wire, put it into a flame (use a gas flame or an alcohol lamp, not a candle). Withdraw the loop, let it cool, then touch it to the colony. Smear this on a microscope slide near one end, add a drop of water, and enlarge the puddle with the loop. Then take another slide and push the end of it into the puddle and draw it across the slide. This will spread the bacteria into a thin film over the length of the slide. Let the slide air dry, then briefly pass the bottom of the slide through a flame. Do not let the surface of the glass get too hot. The whole idea of this procedure is to fix the bacteria to the slide so that they will not wash off in subsequent treatments.

Place a few drops of stain on the surface film and let it stand for thirty seconds to one minute, then rinse the slide in water. Let the slide air dry. It can be viewed directly with an oil immersion objective by putting the oil directly on the fixed, stained film. (An oil immersion objective on a microscope usually has a magnification of 97X and must be coupled to the glass or specimen with immersion oil; that is, the air interface between the glass of the objective and the specimen must be eliminated. Used with a 10X ocular, the total magnification is 970X).

Slides prepared this way will last for a year or so. For more permanence, put a drop of Canada balsam on the film and add a cover glass. A cover glass is an especially thin glass square or rectangle used to protect specimens and provide a flat surface above the specimen on the microscope slide. The space between the cover glass and the microscope slide must be filled with a mounting medium as well as the specimen. If the specimen is to be observed with a 97X objective, then a drop of oil on the cover glass is necessary.

Try crystal violet for stains.

Ammonium oxalate	0.8 gm
Crystal violet	2.0 gm
Ethyl alcohol	20 ml
Water	80 ml

If you cannot find 100% neutral spirits, then use 100 proof vodka as a substitute. Assume 100 proof vodka is equivalent to 50% alcohol, therefore double the "alcohol" and reduce the amount of water appropriately. Dissolve the stain in the alcohol and the oxalate in the water, then mix the two.

The above stain will color all bacteria. With some bacteria the stain can be removed by treating the slide with an iodine-potassium iodide solution (Lugol's solution will do). Those bacteria that retain the stain after this treatment are called Gram positive; those that do not, Gram negative.

The procedure is as follows: Stain with crystal violet for two minutes, rinse the slide, then treat with an iodine-potassium iodide solution for one minute. Rinse the slide and place it in absolute alcohol (100% ethyl alcohol) or wood alcohol (methanol) until decolorized (if it is Gram negative). Rinse the slide and let it dry. You can also counterstain Gram negative bacteria with a 1% safranin solution for five to ten seconds, then wash and dry, which will help visualize them.

10

THE MICROSCOPE

o reveal the miniworlds that exist in the sea and along the shore, you will need the proper tools for exploration and knowledge about how to apply them.

A simple hand lens can uncover the existence and details of structure of a multitude of the smaller invertebrates and larger zooplankton. Simply put the specimens in a shallow dish and illuminate them with a gooseneck lamp or a low-voltage spotlight-type desk lamp.

Your next step might be the acquisition of a low-power stereo microscope with a magnification range from 10X to 30X. This will magnify more than a hand lens and allow you to see coarser details with greater ease.

For the study of fine structures and very small organisms, from diatoms to bacteria, you will need a compound microscope that is capable of magnifications of 50X to 1,000X. Purchased new, these instruments are prohibitively expensive, costing thousands of dollars. Fortunately, older compound microscopes with a monocular eyepiece and requiring an outside light source are available on the used market, priced in the low to mid-hundreds.

To find what you need may require the help of a biologist or hobbyist who can put you in touch with that specialized marketplace. College bulletin boards in the biology department might be a good place to leave a "wanted" request. Do not even consider a "no name" toy. The agony of working with a poorly made device will turn you away from what otherwise can offer you years of revelation and enjoyment.

The monocular microscopes of the 1930s and 1940s made for medical students by Bausch and Lomb, American Optical, Zeiss, and others have common and essential features: standard diameter oculars, objectives with standard Royal Society threads, a revolving nosepiece, coarse and fine focus adjustment, a mechanical stage, an adjustable substage condenser, and a mirror with both a flat and a concave side.

If you plan to use magnification higher than 100X, all these features are essential. Below 100X, you can make do without a mechanical stage and a substage condenser, which will reduce the price of the instrument considerably.

USING THE MICROSCOPE

For low magnification viewing, the source and concentration of light is not critical. Direct the light from any convenient source to the specimen with the mirror. The substage condenser need not be in place (nor-

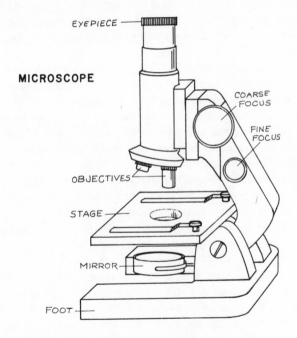

A good "student" microscope with magnifications up to $100 \times$ will provide endless hours of enjoyment.

mally there is a way to swing it out of the beam path). Use the concave side of the mirror; interesting results can be obtained by using oblique illumination. Direct the beam with the mirror (assuming the mirror can be moved from side to side as well as tilted) so that it strikes the specimen at an angle to the lens axis and illuminates the specimen without illuminating the background. The visual result will be a lit specimen against a dark field.

For magnifications above 100X, the light source and the proper use of the substage condenser become crucial. The substage condenser consists of several lenses and may also have two centering screws that alter the position of the condenser's lens axis in relation to the lens axis of the main body of the microscope.

The light source for high magnification microscopy should contain the following elements: a high wattage filament lamp, a condensing lens, an adjustable, or field diaphragm, and a way to adjust the distance between the filament lamp and the condensing lens. When you buy a microscope, don't overlook the cost and availability of a first-rate light source, otherwise you will have no way to get maximum performance out of the microscope.

To resolve maximum detail at high magnification, the specimen must be illuminated so that the full resolving power of the objective is used. To do so requires the proper alignment and adjustment of the light source, mirror, and substage condenser. One way is to set up the system to obtain what has become known as Kohler illumination. When properly done, the resolving power of the objective is fully utilized by providing it with a cone of light equal to that which the objective lens can accept while minimizing image-degrading flare. For convenience, many practicing microscopists affix the microscope and the light source to a common base so that the setup can be quickly duplicated.

A few don'ts: when using higher power objectives don't focus down while watching the image. Bring the objective as close to the specimen as possible, then, watching for the image, focus up. Don't use the iris diaphragm on the substage condenser for light control; use neutral density filters or a rheostat to dim the light source instead. If you open the iris diaphragm too far you will degrade the image with flare, if you close it too far you will degrade the image with diffraction effects.

The usual set of objectives you need are 10X, 43X, and 97X. The 10X and 43X objectives are dry objectives; the 97X objective is an oil immersion objective. If the substage condenser and objective have a numerical aperture higher than 1.0, you must also couple the condenser to the microslide with a drop of oil. To do this put a drop of oil on the top lens of the substage condenser, then raise it until it just touches the slide. Put a drop of oil on the top of the slide and lower the objective into it. After viewing, clean the lenses with soft tissue and lightly wipe them with xylene. If maximum resolution is not necessary, then oil only the objective-slide interface.

SETTING UP KOHLER ILLUMINATION

Mount a microscope slide containing fine structure on the stage. Using a 10X objective, focus on it. Tilt the microscope to a comfortable working angle, but if possible, leave it vertically aligned.

Place the illuminator so that its field diaphragm and condenser are about ten inches from the microscope mirror. Turn the flat side of the mirror toward the illuminator.

Hold a piece of white paper over the mirror. Focus the filament image of the illuminator lamp on the paper by adjusting the distance between the lamp and the illuminator condensing lens. Center the filament image in the microscope mirror.

Remove the paper and swivel the mirror so that the light passes through the substage condenser and strikes the specimen. The light may be so bright that the illumination must be reduced. Do this either by placing a neutral density filter in the beam or dimming the illuminator with a rheostat. (You can make your own neutral density filters by exposing a roll of black-and-white film to an evenly lit flat surface such as a blank wall. Make a series of exposures from three to four stops overexposed to three to four stops underexposed by half stop intervals.

Center the beam in the field of view. If the substage condenser is centerable; that is, if it has adjustment screws that allow it to be aligned with the axis of the microscope optics, then center it by closing down the iris diaphragm on the substage condenser and moving that image to the center of the field.

Rack the substage condenser up until it almost touches the slide on the stage. Readjust the distance between the illuminator lamp and the lamp condenser until a sharp image of the filament is projected on the bottom of the iris diaphragm on the substage condenser. Use a piece of paper and a pocket mirror as aids in doing this.

Close the field diaphragm on the illuminator. Focus the substage condenser until a sharp image of the edge of the diaphragm appears in the field of view. You now have the whole system roughly aligned.

Select a higher objective (43X for example). Focus on the specimen. Refocus the field diaphragm using the substage condenser. Open the field diaphragm until it is just outside the field of view.

Remove the eyepiece and look down the barrel of the microscope. Close down the iris diaphragm on the substage condenser until it just begins to reduce the illumination (about one-quarter of the way closed). Replace the eyepiece and commence viewing.

PREPARING THE SPECIMEN

Specimen preparation is an art and science in itself. The biological literature is filled with specialized techniques for preparing tissues and organisms to emphasize certain features within and between cells. Bacteria require their own special methods. Riffling through a handbook of micro-technique will quickly give you an idea of the kinds and extent of recipes available.

You are unlikely to have or to need the laboratory facilities and chemicals necessary for many procedures. What you do need you can get from a biological supply house. Fortunately, you can make temporary mounts of a great number of specimens and permanent mounts of others with relative ease.

Complicated, permanent mounts require a series of preparative steps: Tissue must be killed and fixed without distortion, stained to reveal specific features, dehydrated and the water replaced with embedding wax, thinly sectioned by slicing with a microtome, and, finally, mounted between a microslide and a cover slip in a hardening medium that will preserve the specimen in a clear state for many years.

Biological supply houses sell a wide variety of prepared slides and, for some, you will find it easier to buy these than to prepare your own.

Permanent mounts of dry material such as fish scales can be made simply by sandwiching the scale between the microslide and the cover slip in a permanent mounting medium like Canada balsam or Hydrax. Permanent mounting media sets by evaporation of a solvent, so leave the preparation flat for several days. Relatively dry material can be mounted in Karo syrup, which is less permanent than Canada balsam, but easier to obtain. It will harden in several days. Trim away the excess around the edge of the cover slip and seal the edges of the cover slip with colorless nail polish or Damar varnish (available in art supply stores).

For small, whole mounts of material containing water, such as plankton, glycerin jelly is a useful, all-purpose medium. You do not need to dehydrate the specimen. You can prestain the specimen before mounting if you choose and you can seal these mounts well enough for them to last several years.

A typical recipe for glycerin jelly is: Dissolve ten grams of gelatin (plain Knox) in sixty ml of water. It will take some time for the gelatin to swell and dissolve. Add seventy ml of glycerin and one gram of phenol (carbolic acid). Warm and stir the mixture until all ingredients are in solution. The finished recipe should be stored in a wide-mouth container (or better yet, several small, wide-mouth containers) that can be conveniently reheated later in hot water. Glycerin jelly sets when cooled and melts when reheated. You can also cut little cubes of the gel and melt them directly on the microscope slide you intend to use for the mount. To finish up a glycerin jelly mount after it sets, scrape away the excess and seal the edges with nail polish or Damar varnish.

For making permanent or temporary mounts, you will need:

Microscope slides (microslides) 1-by-3 inches
Cover slips (#1½ thickness, round or square)
Medicine droppers
Long pipette (to get to the bottom of your tallest specimen jar)
Bottles and jars (wide-mouth)
Razor blade (single edge)
Dissecting needles (make by inserting a sewing needle in the end
    of a ¼-inch-by-5-inch dowel)
Paper towels
Hotplate (small)
Epsom salts
Formalin
Alcohol
Glycerin jelly
Canada balsam
Xylene

Also make up a few slide chambers. To do this, get some ⅝-inch to ¾-inch diameter "bone" rings (plastic rings about ⅛-inch thick used for sliding curtains on a rod and available from a notions store). Glue the ring to the center of a microscope slide with aquarium cement. When you set a cover slip on top of the ring you have a chamber that is quite useful as a temporary mount.

You need not fill the chamber with liquid. Put a drop containing your specimens on a cover slip and quickly invert it so as to leave the drop suspended from the bottom of the slip. Lower it on to the ring. You can smear the ring with petroleum jelly beforehand and create a sealed chamber that will keep specimens from desiccating and active for several days.

Prior to permanent mounting, living material must be killed and fixed. Exposure to Formalin does both. However, most creatures react violently to Formalin and distort badly before being overcome. You can

SLIDE CHAMBER

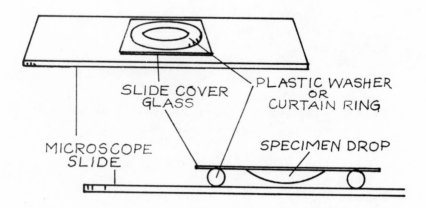

You can keep specimens alive for several days in the hanging drop by ringing the rim with petroleum jelly.

anesthetize your specimen by letting it remain quietly in the presence of Epsom salts. Introduce a few drops at a time of a strong solution of salts until the specimen is completely stunned. Menthol is also useful. Other useful anesthetics have been mentioned in an earlier chapter. Just what works best is a matter of trial-and-error.

Once the specimen is dulled, introduce the Formalin rapidly. If all goes well, the specimen will expire in an expanded state.

Many small organisms are so translucent they can hardly be seen when mounted and put under a microscope. Dyeing the specimen before mounting it will enhance it visually and allow you to see more detail than might otherwise be observable. Dyes for this purpose are called biological stains. All sorts of staining techniques and procedures have been worked out, sometimes using as many as three dyes to stain separate structures in a single tissue. A few dyes can be absorbed by living tissue without being affected by it. Neutral red is one. If you can get some be sure to try it on a living culture.

If you cannot get biological stains, try food coloring. After killing, blot away as much liquid as you can and introduce a strong solution of either a green, blue, or red food dye (or Easter egg dye). Give it a few minutes to stain, then blot away the excess, introduce water, blot again, and repeat the washing until the water surrounding the specimen remains clear. Blot away one more time and introduce warmed glycerin jelly. Breathe heavily on the underside of the cover slip before lowering it on to the specimen. Doing so will lessen the chance of trapping air bubbles in the mounting media. Seal the cover slip as described earlier. The dye may eventually bleed from the specimen, but that will not degrade the image or cause any serious loss of detail.

PHOTOMICROGRAPHY

Taking pictures through the microscope can be done by mounting your camera above the ocular on a firm stand and providing a relatively light-tight coupling between the ocular and the camera lens. The camera lens must be placed as close to the ocular as possible. Alternatively, if you do not use high magnifications, you can remove the camera lens entirely. Couple the camera to the ocular by using extension tubes. Make the space between the extension tube and the ocular light-tight by creating a funnel of black cloth held to the extension tube and the ocular with rubber bands.

Again, a 35-mm single-lens reflex camera with an internal light meter is the easiest to use. The only problem with it is its focal plane shutter, which at slow speeds may cause vibration. If you have enough light for a short exposure, fine; if not, use neutral density filters or a rheostat on the light source to lengthen the exposure time to five to ten seconds. Use a cable release.

If you want to use color film you will have to use a film meant for tungsten illumination and you cannot dim the illumination with a rheostat because that will lower the color temperature of the light source well below what the film was designed for.

Many complications can arise in photomicrography. The best overall explanation of these problems and how to overcome them can be found in Delly's book, *Photography Through the Microscope* (see references).

11

PHOTOGRAPHY

Wherever you go, whatever you collect, and whenever you conduct an experiment that has a visual aspect to it, you will likely decide to record the place, thing, or event using photography. Scenes, sights, and actions that have faded from memory can be refreshed by a photograph. Remember, however, to write down in your log those bits of information that help explain your photos. Pictures alone do not guarantee that you will have total recall forever.

Much of your photography will be straightforward. If you do not already understand the essentials of operating a camera, selecting film, composing a picture, and the like, you should seek do-it-yourself manuals and advice from a photo-supply dealer. Aside from the fundamentals, they can also provide information on more specialized techniques: fill-in flash to soften harsh shadows and help separate the subject from the background; close-up methods that will allow you to fill the negative or transparency with useful images; flare-free aquarium photography; and photomicrography, taking pictures through a microscope.

You can master each of these specialized areas by reading about how it's done, getting equipment that you can afford but that doesn't compromise your goals, and practicing. Don't overlook practice, and don't spare the film. Keep notes on what you are doing; every picture, good or bad, should teach you something.

PHOTOGRAPHY AT SEA

The first rule of sea photography is keep your equipment dry. Seawater and camera gear don't get along well together. If you plan to shoot pictures on a deck drenched in spray, encase your camera in a clear plastic bag. Use rubber bands to snugly close the bag opening which should be placed in the rear or to one side of the camera. Using a UV filter to protect the front element of the lens, fit a rubber band over the forward end of the lens, then remove the plastic directly in front of the UV filter. You can do much the same for an electronic flash except that there is no need to remove the clear plastic in front of the flashtube.

If you are whalewatching, sealwatching, or turtlewatching and cannot approach too close, you will need a telephoto lens. To get sharp photos you must prevent camera vibration. Shoot at the highest shutter speed you can ($\frac{1}{250}$ second and up). For lenses up to 200 mm steady the camera by firmly bracing the arm with which you adjust focus. Put your elbow on your chest and press your body against any convenient vertical deck member. Pressing a raised foot against the ship's rail will also help. For lenses up to 400 mm, a gunstock or monopod is necessary. It might be possible to use a tripod but its use on board ship is very awkward.

If your quarry is something brought alongside, for example a shark about to be tagged, consider using fill-in flash. The dark, dorsal surface of a large fish against a deep green or blue sea on an overcast day doesn't offer much visual contrast and flash will enhance it. Even on a sunny day, the highlights created by a flash will give your photo added sparkle.

Assuming the flash will remain attached to the camera and your exposure time is set at the highest flash synchronization speed (usually either $\frac{1}{60}$ or $\frac{1}{125}$ second) you can only alter the calculated exposure by reducing the flash output (via a control on the flash, adding a diffuser, or covering the flashtube with a layer of handkerchief) if it exceeds the highest f-stop setting on the lens. If the guide number (GN) calcuated f-stop is the same or less than the f-stop indicated by your light meter, go ahead and shoot at the meter f-stop reading; if higher, shoot at the GN f-stop. In the former case, the flash may only be partially effective; ambient light will govern the exposure. In the latter instance, the flash illumination will outweigh natural light.

If you bring aboard small or fragile specimens and decide to do aquarium photography on the spot, you will need several portable, unbreakable aquaria. You can make these from clear ¼-inch plastic which is easy to cut on a table saw (use a veneer blade; a fine-toothed saw)

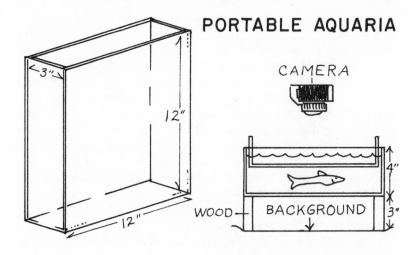

PORTABLE AQUARIA

You can assemble clear plastic aquaria with silicone aquarium cement.
Note that by floating a lid on a horizontal chamber you can eliminate
surface ripples and reflections.

and simple to assemble with silicone aquarium cement. Both a narrow,
vertical tank and a shallow, horizontal tank fitted with a floating lid
through which you will photograph the specimen will come in handy.
Also a sheet of plastic that will fit inside the vertical tank (to restrict the
movement of active animals) is useful. Remember to bring rectangles
of matte black, dark blue, or green oilcloth, or flexible plastic to use as
background. Paper will do but it changes shade as it gets wet (and it
will get wet).

You will probably use sunlight as your only light source for outdoor
aquarium photography. You could use electronic flash but it is difficult
to place the units so as to avoid hot spots on the plastic. In open sunlight
you may have to shade the tank to avoid glare. You may also be able to
reduce reflections by using a polarizing filter. If you cannot seem to
eliminate a front surface reflection of bright objects at or behind the
camera, take a matte black piece of cardboard about 8-by-10 inches or

larger and cut a hole in the center that will just fit over the camera lens. Photograph the scene with this taped to the periphery of the lens.

Using a dark background, either black or deep blue, will also cut down reflections. Be sure to place the background so it is out of focus in the scene.

If you have a camera fitted with a macro lens, you can photograph objects one-half inch or longer and fill most of the picture frame with useful image. If you have a camera with a conventional lens you must use auxiliary equipment. What you choose to use depends on how much of the frame you want occupied by the image of the object you are photographing. The average 35 mm camera equipped with a standard 50 mm lens will just about focus on an object 39 inches away and reproduce that object as an image about one-twentieth of its real size on the film. The field size at that distance is roughly 19-by-29 inches.

One way to quickly judge what equipment you will need is to estimate the field size you want, then select either the supplementary lens or extension tube that most closely approaches it.

Supplementary lenses can be used singly or in combination and do not alter exposure. With the camera lens set at infinity, a +2 diopter lens will give a field size of 9-by-14 inches; a +3 lens, 6-by-9 inches; and a +2 and +3 in tandem, 4-by-6 inches.

The alternative to supplementary lenses is to extend the distance between the lens and the film by using extension tubes. These usually come in sets of three with typical lengths of 8 mm, 16 mm, and 32 mm. With the camera lens set at its point of closest focus, an 8 mm tube will give a field size of 6-by-9 inches and call for a half-stop increase in exposure; a 16 mm tube will give a field size of 3-by-4½ inches and a one-stop increase; and a 32mm tube will give a field size of 1½-by-2½ inches and a 1½ stop increase.

With either method or with a macro lens, the depth of field, the zone in front and back of the plane of sharpest focus, shrinks rapidly as the field size is reduced.

UNDERWATER PHOTOGRAPHY

If you are a proficient free diver (that is, you can hold your breath for a minute-and-a-half at a depth of twenty feet or so) or a scuba diver, you may want to consider underwater photography, but do not do so until you are truly at ease below and can concentrate on the tasks the camera will demand. The camera must become a natural extension of your head, hands, and eyes.

The principles of underwater photography are an extension of those for land photography, but with added stress and limitations imposed by the environment. You can buy a camera and electronic flash especially made for underwater work such as the Nikonos series of cameras, lenses, and strobes, or you can buy housings for the better known above-water 35 mm cameras and strobes. As model changes have taken place, a market in used equipment has also developed. Your choices depend upon what area of underwater photography you wish to concentrate, because no one unit seems to perform all underwater photographic tasks equally well.

The Nikonos design and encased 35 mm cameras preclude through-the-lens viewing, which creates a complication in close-up·photography. How do you find the outline of the scene and how far away is it from the front of the lens? For extreme close-ups using extension tubes (only one extension tube can be used per dive), each tube has a wire frame-finder attached to it that outlines the scene and defines the plane of sharpest focus. This system is fine for sedentary life that is not easily disturbed, but of little use if the animal will not tolerate the close approach of the wires. For those instances you might have to use a supplementary lens coupled with an accurate viewfinder.

With the exception of very shallow, clear water you will need the supplementary light of one or two electronic flash units. One must be connected by cable to the camera to synchronize with its shutter; the other can be fired by the flash of the first unit using a "slave" trigger.

You can take photographs by available light in clear water if the sun is near its zenith. Underwater, the illumination falls very rapidly as the sun's angle decreases relative to the water's surface. You can silhouette your subject against the bright sea surface but the utility of such photos is limited.

The properties of seawater that affect photography are important to know. Objects in water either appear magnified or appear closer by a factor of 1.3. The camera will also "see" this effect, so set underwater lens distances by apparent distance, not measured distance.

The composition of sunlight is profoundly altered with depth. Its red component is rapidly absorbed, while ultra-violet and blues are barely affected. Your eye adjusts to this diminution of reds, but the camera film does not. Available light pictures taken in the clearest water under a full sun have a bluish cast to them that increases rapidly from ten feet down.

Seawater in coastal regions appears green, the consequence of the scattering effect of particles and the presence of "yellow substance," a colorant derived from certain minute plankton abundant in these waters.

Coastal waters are often filled with plankton and other particulates. If you use electronic flash and the flash is close to the camera lens, your photos may be filled with tiny bright dots; reflected light backscattered from the particulates into the lens. To cure this, move the flash away from the camera or illuminate the scene from the side.

Another way to reduce backscatter and the effects of murky water is to use a short focal length lens that has a much wider-than-normal angle of view. This allows you to close in on the subject, reducing the lens-to-subject distance and minimizing the effects of the turbid water.

When you start out in underwater photography, concentrate on one or two useful field sizes, one brand of film, one film speed and one electronic flash output, that is, one guide number setting. By trial-and-error, find the best exposure conditions for both field sizes. Make sure you are using a flash strong enough to yield high f-stop settings (small lens apertures) to get maximum depth of field. For example, for fish pictures, use a distance of 2.75 feet for large ones and 1 foot for small ones; the latter will require a supplementary lens. You will miss many a picture that needed a smaller or much larger field of view, but you will get good photos of many fish and invertebrates that fall within those alloted zones.

12

PHYSICAL AND CHEMICAL MEASUREMENTS ON SEAWATER

he vision conjured up of the working physical oceanographer includes a deep sea vessel equipped with satellite navigation devices, two or three specialized sonars, winches, drums of wire, BT's (bathythermographs), automatic samplers, an on-board laboratory, and a host of other complex paraphernalia.

That vision hardly fits a small runabout and a lone investigator. If you limit your operating depth to 100 feet or so, you can gather much of the same kind of information that the physical oceanographer seeks, but with far simpler equipment.

Although by comparison with today's deep water techniques, the methods given here are old-fashioned, they are still eminently suitable to shallow water. They work as well, albeit not as precisely, and they do not involve the same degree of maintenance and calibration as do their more recent, automatic, digital readout cousins.

Using a sounding line you can determine depth. Old-timers used to put a spot of tallow on the bottom of the lead to find out what kind of bottom they were over at the same time. Naturally, if you have a depth finder you can use that assuming its accuracy is as good or better than a line.

You can attach a Secchi disk to the lead line and estimate top water clarity. By doing this you could measure the extent of an algae bloom or a sewage plume or the seasonal changes in plankton population.

Salinity measurements in an estuary can be used to trace the effects of heavy fresh water runoff or, conversely, the effects of drought. Fresh water runoff can be tracked offshore where its course will be affected by seawater circulation and wind. An invading tongue of salty water underneath river runoff can also be mapped.

Dissolved oxygen is the single most important measure of the health of the body of water. You can use a simple kit or an oxygen probe. With either you can follow seasonal fluctuations in dissolved oxygen (DO), track the effects of sewage, and monitor the presence of excess nutrients in water.

Other analyses are also possible, but you may need access to materials rarely found outside chemical laboratories. Barring those difficulties, environmentalists and naturalists have conducted physical and chemical surveys to shed light on local questions.

SOUNDING LINE

Obtain 100 feet of ⅜-inch manila hemp. Nylon should be avoided; it stretches too much under tension. Eye-splice a ⅜-inch rope thimble at each end. At one end add a No. 1 swivel-eye, safety, snap hook. If splicing rope proves too difficult, tie the swivel on with two half hitches, then lash the loose end of the line to the standing part with waxed thread (dental floss works well). If manila line is too expensive, use braided synthetic clothesline.

Mark the rope off in meters. Begin your measurements from the tip of the swivel eye snap. Mark each meter with a brightly colored plastic tie interwoven between the manila strands. Use a different color on the tenth marker (ten meters). If many of your measurements will be gathered in shallow water, mark off a section of boat railing in tenths of a meter. By grabbing the down line at the waterline and measuring the distance to the next mark, you can estimate the depth to a tenth of a meter.

SOUNDING LEAD

Take a four to five pound scuba weight and drill a ⁷⁄₁₆-inch hole on center through it. Thread a ⅜-inch-by-5-inch galvanized eyebolt through the hole. Add a washer and nut, and tighten. This weight can also be used to carry a Secchi disk below.

SECCHI DISK

Cut an 8-inch diameter disk of ⅜-inch plywood. Drill a ⁷/₁₆-inch hole through its center. Paint the disk with two coats of flat white enamel.

You can mount the disk between the sounding lead weight and the eyebolt. When attached to the sounding line and lowered over the side it will descend parallel to the surface.

DETERMINING SEA WATER CLARITY

The Secchi disk is used to estimate the transparency of seawater. Lower it over the side and measure the depth at which it just disappears. Raise it until it is just visible. Measure that depth. Record the average of the two readings.

The Secchi disk is subject to error. The height to the deck can alter the reading by as much as two meters. A cloudy day as well as a low sun reduces the apparent visibility of the disk.

The clarity of coastal seawater will vary seasonally and differ from inshore to offshore. Long Island sound might show a disk depth of 2.6 meters while in a clear, Caribbean sea a disk depth of 41 meters is not uncommon.

SAMPLING THE DEEP

For water samples from depths of thirty meters or less, the Meyer's bottle works well and is inexpensive. Get a half-gallon wine bottle or something of similiar shape with an opening that can be plugged with a No. 6 one-holed rubber stopper. Thread a ¼-inch-by-3-inch galvanized eyebolt on to which you have first placed a nut and washer, through the stopper. Add a second washer and nut, and tighten. Check the fit in the bottle opening. It should be snug and not in so far that outside pressure will force it through the neck of the bottle.

Cut a four-foot length of ⅛-inch synthetic line and tie the eyebolt with stopper attached to the center of the line. Giving the stopper three to four inches of free play, strap the two ends of the lines to opposing sides down the length of the bottle with galvanized wire or strong twine. Cover the wire with waterproof electrician's tape to help secure the wire and line to the bottle. Tie the loose ends of the line to a snap ring or a shackle.

To use the bottle, attach the sounding lead to the snap ring and the sounding line to the eyebolt. Insert the stopper in the bottle and lower to the appropriate depth. Give the line a hard tug which will pull the stopper out of the bottle and fill it with your water sample. As you haul it up very little exchange will take place between the inside contents and the surrounding water.

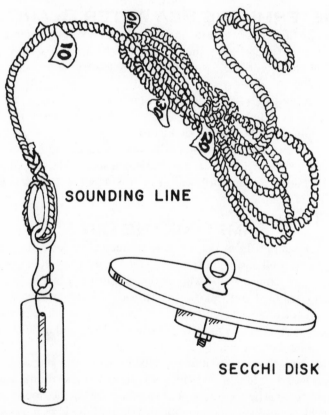

SOUNDING LINE

SECCHI DISK

The sounding line need not be marked in parts of a meter. Lay out a finer scale along the rail of the boat and use that to find fractional lengths.

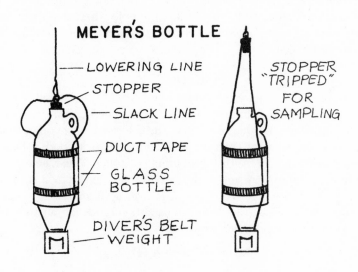

The Meyer's bottle will work well to 30 meters. Below that you will need more elaborate collecting equipment.

TEMPERATURE MEASUREMENT

Water temperature measurement is relatively straightforward, however, whatever thermometer you choose for your measurements should occasionally be calibrated against a standard. A mixture of ice and fresh water will do as a 0°C or 32°F checkpoint. The thermometer can also be checked against a short-range clinical thermometer in the 97 to 104°F region.

Alcohol- and mercury-filled thermometers are fragile. You may find a bimetallic thermometer like those used for film developing sturdier than a glass thermometer in the field.

If you do use a glass thermometer, you can prevent it from breaking by either purchasing or making a storage container for it. A length of ¼-inch PVC pipe with a pipe cap on one end and a stopper on the other will do well. Stuff a bit of cloth in the bottom and put a plastic straw down the pipe to keep the thermometer from rattling around in transit.

Be sure to check the liquid column in your thermometer regularly. Make sure the column of liquid is intact. If not, put it in icewater or in a freezer to contract all the liquid into the bulb where it will become continuous again. A shake may help, but be careful it doesn't snap the thermometer stem.

SALINITY

The salinity of seawater can be inferred from density-temperature measurements (as is done in the chapter on aquariums) or more precisely by measuring its chlorinity. Chlorinity, the chloride content of seawater, is remarkably constant (barring local anomalies from odd pollution sources) at 55.29% of the dissolved inorganic solids of seawater.

Chloride ion in seawater is measured by titration using a standard solution of silver nitrate and potassium chromate as an indicator. When silver nitrate is added to a solution containing chloride ion, an insoluble precipitate of silver chloride forms.

$$A_g^+ + Cl^- \rightarrow A_gCl \downarrow$$

You measure the amount of silver ion consumed to just reach the point where all the chloride ion in a known volume of seawater has been converted into a precipitate. From that, you can calculate the original chloride concentration.

The method for measuring salinity by chloride titration is given in the appendix. The analysis can also be done with a commercially available test kit which is easy to use at sea.

CHEMICAL ANALYSIS

Full chemical analysis of seawater is beyond the means of the marine naturalist. However, a number of discrete measurements are possible with simple kits and common laboratory apparatus.

Before attempting to analyze anything, carefully consider what the results may mean and how you intend to use them. What will be your standards of comparison? What significance can you attach to differences between your measurements and those standards?

Are analyses warranted? For example, you might monitor an aquarium using nitrite-nitrate data. That is a must if you are dealing with a 20,000-gallon system, but is it worth it for a 20-gallon setup? (The answer may be "yes" if you are curious about the carrying capacity of the aquarium.)

Dissolved oxygen (DO) and Biochemical Oxygen Demand (BOD) analyses lend themselves to a number of environmental studies, and emphasis has been placed on their measurement.

For field studies, the single most important measurable component of seawater is dissolved oxygen. From its analysis and the water temperature, you can infer the immediate state of health of creatures living in it. By holding water samples in the dark over a period of time and measuring the decrease in dissolved oxygen you can infer the nutrient load in the water.

DISSOLVED OXYGEN

The dissolved oxygen content of water is critical to the life within it. Each species has its own tolerance range; higher forms, such as fish, usually are distressed by hypoxic water (less than 2 mg of oxygen per liter) while some invertebrates can put up with anoxic water (less than 0.1 mg oxygen per liter) for short periods of time. Anoxic conditions are often followed by sulfiding, the formation of hydrogen sulfide, which is poisonous to all life except some specialized bacteria and deep sea forms.

The dissolved oxygen content of seawater depends upon its temperature and, to a far lesser extent, its salinity.

SATURATION VALUES OF OXYGEN IN SEAWATER (ML /1)
Salinity (parts per thousand)

Temperature (C)	27	31	34
0°	8.6	8.3	8.1
10°	6.8	6.6	6.4
20°	5.6	5.5	5.4
30°	4.7	4.6	4.5

Although oceanographers prefer to report dissolved oxygen (DO) in milliliters per liter (as above), the chemist measures DO in milligrams per liter (mg /1). To convert from mg /1 to ml /1, multiply mg /1 by 0.7.

Dissolved oxygen content is often reported as parts per million (ppm) which is equivalent to mg /1, not ml /1.

DO ANALYSIS

Sea water can be analyzed for DO either chemically by titration or electrochemically by an oxygen probe. The chemical method is slower and subject to error from interfering substances, but has the advantage of independence from salinity and is considerably less expensive initially. At this writing, a simple DO analysis kit, capable of fifty measurements, cost a little over $25, while a low-priced dissolved oxygen meter and probe costs over $200.

The initially high cost of the oxygen probe is justifiable if you plan to do a great number of either DO or BOD analyses. Even so, you may need the chemical method to verify the accuracy of the probe technique.

SAMPLING

Samples must be drawn without altering their dissolved oxygen content, and either immediately read with the probe or "fixed" chemically to prevent any changes between the time of collection and the time of analysis. This is critical if the deck temperature is considerably different than the water temperature.

The volume of sample needed depends on the concentrations of the specific reagents used and is typically between 50 and 300 ml. (The analytical method presented in the appendix calls for a 300 ml sample.) DO kits, which will be discussed next, call for a sample of 60 ml.

Fill the sample bottle to the brim without aerating the inflowing water. Cap the sample bubble-free. To collect a sample below water, use the sampler already discussed or a unit that descends open at both ends and snaps shut at the appropriate depth. If you collect samples while diving, descend with the sample bottle open. At depth, exchange the water in the bottle with local water using a syringe (a big turkey baster works well). If you simply open up an empty bottle and let the water rush in, the air in the bottle will aerate the sample.

CHEMICAL METHOD

The chemical method now universally used is called the azide modification of the classical Winkler method. The basis of this method is as follows: a manganous sulfate and alkaline hydroxide-iodide-azide solution are added to the water sample. A white precipitate of manganous hydroxide initially forms which reacts with the dissolved oxygen forming a brown manganic hydroxide. This "fixes" the dissolved oxygen. The sample is then (or later) acidified with either sulfuric or sulfamic acid. Free iodine, which instantly forms triiodide ion, is released in proportion to the sample's oxygen content. An aliquot of the treated sample is titrated with a standard sodium thiosulfate solution using a starch indicator. The solution remains black until all the iodine has been transformed to iodide ion by the thiosulfate. The endpoint is a colorless solution. In chemical shorthand, the stepwise reactions are:

$$Mn^{++} + 2\,OH^- \rightarrow Mn(OH)_2$$
$$2\,Mn(OH)_2 + O_2 \rightarrow 2\,MnO(OH)_2$$
$$MnO(OH)_2 + 4\,H^+ + 2\,I^- \rightarrow Mn^{++} + I_2 + 3\,H_2O$$
$$I_2 + 2\,S_2O \rightarrow 2\,I^= + S_4O_6^=$$

DISSOLVED OXYGEN METER

The Winkler Method is subject to error from a number of interferences: free chlorine, iron, high suspended solids, readily oxidized organics,

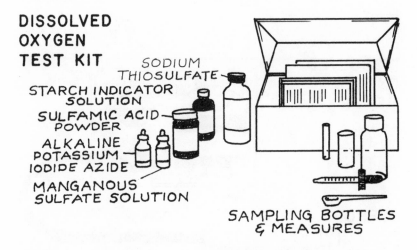

DISSOLVED OXYGEN TEST KIT

SODIUM THIOSULFATE

STARCH INDICATOR SOLUTION

SULFAMIC ACID POWDER

ALKALINE POTASSIUM IODIDE AZIDE

MANGANOUS SULFATE SOLUTION

SAMPLING BOTTLES & MEASURES

If you can follow instructions and count drops you can use this kit with ease.

untreated sewage, biological flocs, and color; the DO meter and probe are not. A number of scientific instrument makers market reliable DO devices: Bausch and Lomb, Yellow Springs Instruments (YSI), and Beckman are well known. Manufacturers claim 0.1 mg /1 repeatability with 0.1% accuracy.

The DO probe operates on an electrochemical principle. Inside the probe a voltage is applied across a gold cathode and a silver anode immersed in a potassium chloride electrolyte. The inside of the cell probe is separated from the surrounding environment (the sample) by a semi-permiable membrane. Oxygen permiates past that membrane into the cell and reacts at the cathode. The cell reaction produces an electrical current proportional to the oxygen content of the liquid in which the probe is immersed.

Both temperature and salinity affect oxygen transport across the membrane and therefore affect the current produced. Meters generally have built-in compensating circuits for both factors.

The probe takes two to five minutes to reach equilibrium, although a reliable reading can be taken in less than a minute. The probe and meter come with full instructions. Extra membranes will be needed for the probe. They have to be changed every few weeks depending on the nature of the samples.

DISSOLVED OXYGEN METER

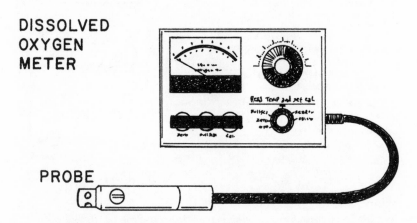

PROBE

If you plan to measure more than ten dissolved oxygen analyses a day over an extended period, a DO meter quickly pays for itself.

Most inexpensive DO meters are not built to withstand the rigors of a saltwater environment, so place the meter in a clear plastic bag and pack the bagged meter into a waterproof box. A small, plastic cooler works well. At the end of the day clean the probe with fresh water.

BIOCHEMICAL OXYGEN DEMAND

Organic matter in rivers, estuaries, and open sea, whose origin is either from natural sources or from man-related waste effluent, will biodegrade by bacterial action and consume dissolved oxygen.

The BOD test is an empirical assay in which the dissolved oxygen content of the water is measured as sampled and again after five days storage at 20°C in the dark in full, stoppered bottles. The reason for dark storage is to prevent any algae from producing oxygen by photosynthesis.

The DO measurement can be done either by the Winkler method or a DO probe. The latter is a much more appropriate way because so many samples are necessary. For polluted water, a series of dilutions must be made with synthetic (and sterile) seawater of the same salinity so that after five days, about 50% of the original (after dilution) DO remains.

This method is subject to considerable variation. An inoculum of microorganisms from a polluted source such as a waste treatment facility will consume oxygen much more rapidly than the natural bacteria in the everyday environment. Thus bacterial action may be so slow in some samples, that BOD has not peaked at the end of five days. The presence of toxins in the sample may have the same effect. No reference standards exist for BOD measurements, nor is test reproducibility good. Nonetheless, the method remains in widespread use.

CHEMICAL OXYGEN DEMAND

Quicker, simpler, more accurate and precise than BOD, COD is based on measuring the oxygen consumed by boiling the sample in sulfuric acid and potassium dichromate, a strong oxidant. Chloride ion interferes with the method, but that can be overcome by adding mercuric sulfate. The COD method is a standard ASTM procedure (D 1252-67). It requires both a fume hood and waste disposal facilities.

TOTAL ORGANIC CARBON

Marine scientists often measure TOC. The sample is vaporized and its carbon content transformed into carbon dioxide which is measured by infra-red analysis. The apparatus is simple to operate but costly to set up.

13

MARINE AQUARIUMS

hether you want to experiment or observe marine life either to study or simply satisfy your curiosity, a marine aquarium will substantially extend your opportunity to do so.

Few of us live close enough to the sea to draw water continuously from it, so by necessity your system will be a closed loop with relatively low volume. For the creatures you put there, it is an artificial environment only superficially akin to the waters from which they were taken. Not only is it foreign to them, but it is subject to rapid change, generally for the worse.

Many species cannot adapt to artificial acculturation. Some may live a few days, then sicken and perish. Others are gone in hours. Jellyfish, comb-jellies, and planktonic forms survive only a few days at most. Fast predator fish do poorly in small confining tanks.

Enough fish and invertebrates do accommodate to aquarium life to allow the leisurely observation and study of a great number of representative forms. The list is long. If you have a definite project in mind, put considerable thought and effort into your choice of animal. One of the hallmarks of successful experimental biology is the selection of the appropriate subject.

In a mixed aquarium, give thought to the compatibility of the species you intermingle. A bivalve will not last long in a tank with a sea star, nor will small fish behave calmly cooped up continually with a blue crab. Crabs are rough on most soft invertebrates in an aquarium and some are hard on the aquarium itself, continually heaping and churning the bottom gravel, destroying the efficiency of the filtration system.

REPRESENTATIVE INVERTEBRATES THAT DO WELL IN AQUARIUMS

Species	Class
Cordylophora lacustris	Hydrozoa
Cassiopea frondosa	Syphozoa
Anthropleura xanthogrammica	Anthozoa
Metridium senile	Anthozoa
Nereis sp.	Annelida
Ilyanassa obsoleta	Gastropoda
Mytilus sp.	Bivalva
Limulus polyphemis	Arthropoda
Cancer, Crangon, Uca sp.	Crustacea
Asterias forbesi	Asteroida
Arbacia punctulata	Echinoida

EQUIPMENT AND SETUP

All-glass tanks, preassembled with silicone adhesive, and available from 5- to 100-gallon capacities, are inexpensive for salt water work. Do not buy anything smaller than a 20-gallon size for your main tank, although one or two smaller ones may come in handy for photography. Plastic buckets will do for holding tanks.

Glass tanks come in a standard low form and high form. Although the squatter low form has a somewhat higher surface-to-volume ratio and is generally recommended for that reason, the high form is more useful for fish observation and aquarium photography.

Consider tank placement carefully. The location should be cool, but not subject to temperature fluctuation or sunlight. Direct sunlight will over-warm the tank and promote algal growth.

The tank stand should be sturdy, and for large tanks, the flooring substantial. Once filled, the tank is immovable; a 20-gallon aquarium weighs in excess of 170 pounds. Locate the tank where it not apt to be jarred, usually close to a bearing wall.

Before filling it, make sure the base is level. It is a wise move to pretest the tank's watertightness by slowly filling it with tap water some place where a spill will do no harm. To remove water from a tank, siphon it off. Never try to empty it by tipping.

Consider the effects of a major spill. Nearby electrical service will be shorted out, and on a wooden floor, whatever lies below it will be affected. Groups of tanks are often set in a plastic-lined trough equipped with a drain.

Mechanical filtration, biological purification, and aeration, the life support system of the aquarium, are best supplied by a subgravel-airlift rig. The bottom of the tank is outfitted with a raised bed of gravel. Airlifts both oxygenate and circulate the water, and by a skimming mechanism, remove protein waste products from it. The airlift system is so arranged that it draws water down through the gravel bed into the open area beneath, then up to the surface through open, aerated standpipes.

BUILDING A SUBGRAVEL SYSTEM

These units can be purchased or constructed. Your choice depends on how many you will need, your handiness with tools, and economics. The system consists of a perforated plate that fits snugly in the aquarium and is supported off the bottom by small feet that allow free circulation underneath. At the rear corners of the tank, on both sides, airlifts extend from the liquid surface down through the plate. The airlift is a chamber, open beneath the plate, but enclosed above the plate to the surface, in which an airstone sits near the bottom supplied by a hose from above. Water circulates from the bottom to the top, pushed upward by the rising stream of bubbles.

Both Moe and the National Research Council (see references at the end of the book) show plans for constructing these units. Both make use of a plastic, light-diffuser lattice originally intended for fluorescent light fixtures as a base. Support it one inch off the bottom by gluing any convenient inert material to the lattice with aquarium adhesive in such a way that it won't sag under the weight of the gravel and won't impede the flow of water or create "dead spots" in the bottom chamber. Use silicone aquarium cement. Never use bathroom caulk; it contains a fungicide and may affect life in the tank.

After the airlifts are fitted into the lattice or the lattice is cut to clear the corner plates (NRC method), the exposed surface of the plastic is covered with plastic flyscreen which can be tied on with fishermen's nylon monofilament line.

Airlifts are usually fitted into the two extreme rear corners of the tank.

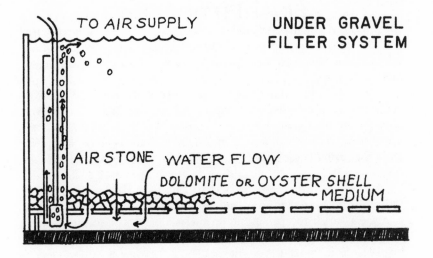

The subgravel filter system is an absolute must for a saltwater aquarium.

Moe uses one-inch, white PVC plastic pipe fitted with an elbow at the surface to direct the outflow and cut down the aspirating effect of the rising bubbles. He fits the pipe through the lattice and perforates it where it extends into the open area below the lattice. A 5/16-inch hole in the top of the elbow allows the passage of an air hose down the pipe to an airstone at the bottom.

Alternatively, NRC glues a 2-inch wide sheet of light plastic catty-corner from just above the liquid surface to one inch from the bottom of the tank in both rear corners. The plastic should have several 1/8-inch vertical slits near the top to allow the upwelling water to escape without allowing the tank critters to investigate the triangular-shaped corner cavity. The airhose and airstone are simply dropped down into the well created by the plastic. The lattice base must have its corners cut off so that it fits snugly against the plastic walls of the airlift.

A 3-inch bed of gravel is placed on the flyscreen. Prewash the gravel in tap water until the water runs clear. Calcareous gravel is best—crushed coral, crushed oyster shell, or dolomite. The average diameter of the stones should be just under ¼-inch.

FINAL FITTING OUT

You will need an air pump, either a large vibrator or piston type. You will also need ³⁄₁₆-inch plastic tubing and at least one set of triple gang valves to distribute and regulate the air flow in the airlifts and accessories.

An outside filter, although not entirely necessary, will help trap particulates and absorb dissolved organic matter. Use an air-lift type. The filler for the filter chamber should consist of polyester "hair" (do not use glass wool) and activated charcoal. Prewash the charcoal in tap water before using it to remove fines.

LIGHTS

Unless the purpose of the aquarium is mainly display, do not illuminate it. Algae flourish too prolifically in most aquariums because of overlighting. If you do choose to use a light, make sure it is well protected by plastic from the effects of salt spray.

Fit a lid, made either of glass or plastic, over the entire top. It need not be one piece, but should cover as much of the aquarium as possible to cut down on evaporation and prevent specimens from leaping out as they are occasionally wont to do. For easy removal of the lid(s), glue plastic handles to them with aquarium cement.

You will also need some odds and ends—a scraper-sponge, a plastic basting syringe or siphon device to remove large particles, a hose for siphoning, and plastic buckets. Do not use these accessories for anything except the aquarium.

Partly fill the aquarium with tap water. Lay a plate or bowl on the gravel to disperse the force of the incoming water. Dissolve the necessary amount of synthetic sea salt in a plastic bucket and add it to the aquarium as a liquid concentrate. Stir it and start your airlifts. Check the salinity with a hydrometer and continue to dilute with tap water until the salinity falls within the proper range.

Run the aquarium for a few days with no specimens in it. Any initial cloudiness should clear up as the filters begin their work. Measure temperature and salinity. When initial conditions are stable, add a few hardy baitfish. You may not intend to keep them, but they will initiate the "conditioning" of the filter bed and transform it into a biologically active purifier.

CONDITIONING

Complex organic compounds from food particles and excretion products of the fish will be broken down into simple compounds by bacteria that will eventually cover the entire surface of the bottom gravel. Initially, heterotrophic bacteria break down the organic matter and produce ammonia which is toxic to fish. Two groups of autotrophic bacteria, Nitrosomas and Nitrobacter, convert the ammonia stepwise to nitrite and then to nitrate where it is either used by denitrifying bacteria and converted to nitrogen or assimilated by plants or algae.

It can take up to five weeks for an aquarium to come to equilibrium. If you already have another aquarium up and running, you can speed up the process by transferring a little gravel from the old, established tank to the new one.

You can test for both ammonia and nitrite with simple test kits. The aquarium is not "safe" for sensitive species unless the ammonia level is less than 0.1 ppm and the nitrite level is one to two ppm. Both levels rise as you add more specimens, but, to a point the filter bed will contain the levels within acceptable limits. Remember that the volume of the filter bed is limited, therefore so is the carrying capacity of the aquarium.

Every author on aquarium-keeping has a pet formula for how much the aquarium will tolerate. Three inches of fish per square foot of filter bed is one, but just how that translates into invertebrates isn't clear. Normally, though, invertebrates are more tolerant of nitrogenous by-products than are fish.

Add no more than one or two specimens per week until carrying capacity is approached. This gives the filter bed a chance to reach maximum conversion capacity and all occupants a chance to grow used to the rising toxin levels.

Some animals tolerate the toxins that accumulate in the aquarium water better than others. Judge loading by the behavior of the most sensitive species.

It is a wise idea to get your aquarium experience with inexpensive, local species. However, working successfully with estuarine fish taken from partly polluted waters can lull you into false notions on care level and carrying capacity that might be fatal to more delicate forms.

TEMPERATURE

Fortunately, room temperature (21° to 25° C) will suffice for a great number of species. Sea water temperatures from Cape Cod to central Florida range from 1° C to 25° C. Along the northern shores of the Gulf of Mexico, temperatures range from 13° to 29° C, therefore most species from either waters will accommodate to 18° to 25° C. Southern Florida waters vary seasonally from 22° to 31° C, while Puerto Rican waters are nearly constant at 28° to 30° C. Tropical reef fish from either area will acclimate to 24° to 26° C. The danger of raising the temperature closer to 30° C for tropicals is the decline in maximum dissolved oxygen content of the water to 6.2 ppm which is very close to the 5 ppm point where many species begin to show signs of stress; should marginal conditions prevail in the aquarium, you increase the odds of risking sudden disaster.

From Nova Scotia to Cape Cod on the Atlantic coast, water temperatures range from 2° to 11° C and from Pacific Grove, California to Friday Harbor, Washington, from 7° to 14° C. For many creatures from these waters, cooler 12° C temperatures are mandatory, therefore the aquarium water must be chilled. You can build such a setup using an old refrigerator to hold and cool the aquarium or you can circulate chilled water to an insulated aquarium outside. Neither project is particularly easy.

SALINITY CONTROL

Salinity is the weight of total dissolved solids in 1,000 grams of seawater or, put another way, the weight of dissolved salts in parts per thousand (0/00 or ppt). Open sea salinity averages thirty-four to thirty-five ppt while coastal water runs in the mid to upper twenties.

You can set your aquarium anywhere between twenty-five to thirty-two ppt. Try to reasonably match the water from which you obtained your specimens. For aquariums, the measurement of salinity need only be approximate. We can use an indirect measure, the specific gravity of the seawater. Specific gravity is the ratio of the weight of a given volume of seawater to an equal volume of distilled water. This ratio is measured with a hydrometer, a weighted glass bulb with a calibrated stem. It floats

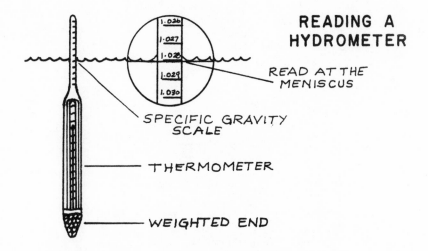

READING A HYDROMETER

READ AT THE MENISCUS

SPECIFIC GRAVITY SCALE

THERMOMETER

WEIGHTED END

The combination hydrometer-thermometer will give you all the information you need to set the salinity of your aquarium.

in the water, stem up, sinking to a depth that depends on the dissolved solids in the water and the water temperature. Most hydrometers are calibrated at 15° C, therefore a correction factor must be applied to the reading if the water is warmer or cooler. The accompanying chart will help. The parallelogram encloses the preferred salinity-temperature range.

PHOTOGRAPHY

You can use a wide variety of cameras for aquarium photography, but for speed and ease of operation it is hard to beat a 35-mm single-lens reflex equipped with an internal light meter and a 50-mm macro lens. That combination allows you to concentrate on subject matter and composition rather than fuss about the technical problems of focus, framing, and exposure.

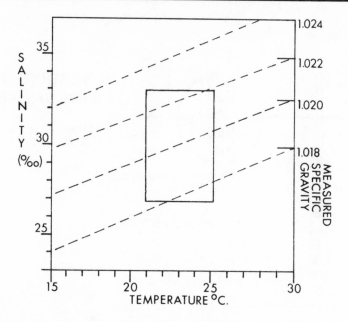

Relationship between salinity-temperature and measured specific gravity for a hydrometer calibrated at 15° C. The dotted lines are lines of constant specific gravity. The preferred temperature-salinity ranges for the average aquarium fall within the rectangle.

Small, sluggish creatures are easier to photograph if you transfer them from your main tank to shallower quarters where you can position them as you please. Long before your shooting session you will have to coax sessile attached creatures off the walls of the main tank on to another solid but transferable substrate such as a small sheet of glass or a stone.

Once in a small aquarium, you can move the whole rig outdoors and use natural light. You can fill in shadows by bouncing sunlight off white cardboard. Other cardboard will come in handy for shading the front glass surface of the aquarium and providing background. A few minutes viewing with a camera will convince you that unwanted surface reflections off the glass will be your major problem. Look for them before you shoot. It is possible to be so absorbed by the subject that you ignore glare and streaks of light that look unassuming in the viewer but will ruin the picture. You can avoid them by a combination of shading and lens placement.

Let's assume you plan to photograph fish indoors in your main aquarium. A few hours before you plan to begin shooting, clean the glass inside and out. For the outside use glass cleaner—do not spray it directly at the aquarium but into a wiping cloth because overspray might drift into the tank and stress the fish. Clean the inside with your sponge-scraper and remove any algae growing on the walls. Tape matte black paper to the outside back wall of the aquarium for background (or dark blue if you prefer). Clear away the aquarium light fixture or lid and mount either an incandescent photo lamp or your electronic flash above the tank as close to the front wall as possible, tilted slightly rearward. Check to be sure that the light does not spill down the outside of the front wall of the aquarium. The light should flood downward and backward. You may have to tape a "lip" of cardboard along the top front edge of the aquarium to get what you want.

Now go away for a while and let the occupants settle down. When they seem ready and do not skitter at the least disturbance, follow them with the camera placed as close to the front glass as possible. Be sure you have blocked off any extraneous sources of light, especially those in back of you. Expose at the highest exposure speed you can, not only to stop action, but to throw the background out of focus. Always shoot with the lens axis perpendicular to the glass. If you tilt the camera you risk reflection problems.

If you have an automatic exposure feature on your electronic flash, the black background will fool the internal meter into delivering too much light, so override the exposure and reduce it by one full stop or set the film speed to double its actual value.

Keep a record of how you handled the setup and your exposure data so that you can learn from your errors. No sense making the same mistake in your next shooting session.

Above all, be patient. You are unlikely to get just what you want the first time around, not only because the fish refuse to cooperate, but also because you must learn what you are looking for.

14

STUDIES YOU CAN DO

The way nature works offers constant surprise and continual opportunities to reveal those workings. You can often uncover them for yourself with a minimum of scientific equipment.

At first, you may feel at a disadvantage compared to a professional biologist. After all, you have had less formal training in the biological sciences, less access to a science library, and few interrelationships with other scientists.

You can overcome these disadvantages by study on your own and by developing associations with scientists and naturalists through environmental organizations and your local museum, aquarium, or university.

You may have some distinct advantages over a professional biologist—skill in a related field and the time and energy to devote to a problem of your own choosing.

Over the past three decades, the American Littoral Society publication *Underwater Naturalist* has printed field notes, reports, and studies done by amateur naturalists as well as professional biologists.

Let us look at a brief sampling of articles from UN and see how you might have done the same thing. As you read these articles, ask yourself what you would need to know before you could recognize an unusual occurrence or previously unknown behavior pattern. If you were doing the observing, what questions would you ask? What explanations would you eliminate? What would you have tried to prove or disprove?

Some articles have been abbreviated, reduced to their major content and essential points. We start with field notes; basically descriptions of occurrences and behavior, some new to the authors and some reasonably normal events.

Kolator finds conger eel larvae in an unusual place. Grant comes upon *Grammarus* spawning. Mountford describes fall bioluminescence in a tidal bay.

Beyond the field note is the study that asks a question, presents evidence, and draws a conclusion. Steimle and Geer, and a long list of helpers, decide to find out what is in a polluted bay and discover it still has plenty of life in it.

Often a project requires lab work. O'Neill and others measured the BOD rise of nuclear power plant effluent caused by a "Waring Blendor" effect from biological entrainment in its cooling waters and came up with surprisingly high numbers. In the final paper, Moroff and Kane look at littoral sand size variations on Long Island. As you read about the methods they employ, ask yourself about the nature of beach sand. Are the grains always rounded? Is the sand usually made up of one mineral? If it contained two minerals in equal amounts but significantly different in specific gravity, would sieve weights accurately reflect the number of grains per unit volume?

"THE OCCURRENCE OF CONGER EEL LARVAE IN A NEW JERSEY ESTUARY," by D. Kolator, *Underwater Naturalist*, Vol. 10, No. 2

On separate beach seines during the spring of 1976, three congrid leptocephali were captured in the Shark River estuary, Belmar, New Jersey. The leptocephali were identified as conger eel, *Conger oceanicus* (Fahay, pers. comm., Sandy Hook Laboratory, Highlands, New Jersey). The estuary is located in Monmouth County, central New Jersey. It connects with Shark River Inlet, a narrow channel 122 m wide, which empties into the Atlantic Ocean. The estuary itself is about 3.00 km long and 2.17 km wide. It is a shallow basin 0.6 m at mean low water, with several narrow channels (2.3 m at mean low water) paralleling most of its shore line. The mean tidal range is about 1.0 m, and the water temperature ranges seasonally from 0.0° C to 22.4° C. The salinity ranges from 31.74 to 25.57 ppt. A 50-foot seine was used to collect the sample.

Two of the larvae were captured approximately 6.1 m from the southwestern end of Shark River Island, a spoil heap located near the eastern end of the estuary. The tide was incoming and had a salinity of 31.43 ppt and a temperature of 12.5° C. They were captured in 0.6 m of water. One leptocephalus was 88 mm in total length, having 141 myomeres; the other was 91 mm in total length, having 145 myomeres. The third was captured 9.1 m off the shore at MacLearie Park Beach. It was captured in approximately 0.6 m of water during a flood tide which had a salinity of 31.18 ppt and a temperature of 13.0° C. This sample was 95 mm in total length, having 146 myomeres.

Conger eel leptocephali are rarely found in estuaries. They are more common in the Gulf of Maine and are found in the western North Atlantic. Many have been washed ashore along New England beaches and they have been captured in large estuaries, such as the Chesapeake Bay, Delaware Bay, and Montsweag Bay, Maine, the former in low salinity water, 26 ppt. I have yet to find reports of conger eel leptocephali captured in New Jersey waters. Conger eel leptocephali reportedly grow 150–160 mm in length. The specimens in Shark River were in the metamorphose stage since the gut of each had shortened and their snouts were broader and more rounded.

"SCUD SPAWNING," D. Grant, *Underwater Naturalist,* Vol. 15, No. 1

Several evenings this past summer (1983), swarms of scuds were observed in the surface waters of Sandy Hook Bay. At 6:30 P.M., July 8, a particularly large concentration was observed near the middle of the bay. We estimated that for a quarter mile, our vessel passed through densities of 250 or more individuals per square meter. Visibility from the surface was excellent (over six feet); temperature and salinities were: 24.2° C and 24 ppt; 23.3° C and 24.2 ppt (bottom, twenty feet), and the surface was very calm. High tide was predicted at 10:12 P.M.

Surprisingly, there was no evidence of any fishes or birds taking advantage of the swarm. The majority concentrated 12 to 18 inches below the surface and actively avoided attempts at capture with a dip-net.

Fortunately, two specimens were netted. Like many in the swarm, they were coupled and remained so after capture. The

male (17 mm) carried the female (12 mm). They were later identified as *Gammarus annulatus,* an essentially pelagic amphipod
of New England, Cape Cod, and Long Island Sound. *G. annulatus*
has previously been reported from power plant intake screens
along Raritan Bay. They appear to be annual and ovigerous females have been collected from June through September. This
lengthy spawning season could explain their behavior at the surface.

BIOLUMINESCENCE IN BARNEGAT BAY, K. Mountford, *Underwater Naturalist,* Vol. 2, No. 1

Newspapers in the summer of 1963 made reference to brilliant
phosphorescence in waters off the Jersey shore. No apparent mention was made of the phenomenon in Barnegat Bay where the
intensity reached fantastic proportions during a late "bloom" between October twenty-fourth and twenty-seventh.

Copepods of the groups Cyclopoida and Calanoid seemed most
common in a sample taken at that time. These creatures, hundreds per square inch of surface area, strongly luminesced when
agitated. With a friend sweeping the tiller of my twenty-foot boat
to and fro, I was able to kneel on the afterdeck and read the non-
luminous dial of my watch by the resulting light! Swimming fish
moved below, clearly visible, like blue-green comets.

Two qualities of luminescence were simultaneously apparent
during the bloom: easily discernible motes (star phosphorescence) and a diffuse, cloud-like illumination.

Most "star" phosphorescence has been attributed (by Berrill)
to *Noctiluca scintillans,* an armored flagellate, but I have never
found it in my samples. In both Barnegat and adjacent ocean waters, I have traced much "star" phosphoresence directly to members of the order Copepoda. While these tiny crustaceans are not
always luminescent (nor always present together with luminescence) they seem significantly involved in that phenomenon. I
have hypothesized that they may ingest other organisms which
may be the primary source of luminescence.

During a September luminescent bloom off Sandy Hook, Dr.
Jan Prager, microbiologist at the Sandy Hook Marine Lab, isolated

and cultured (at 20°C) a phosphorescent algae *Gonyaulax scrippsae* (Kofoid). This organism was first discovered by Martin during a 1925 study of Barnegat Bay. Dr. Prager believes *Gonyaulax* was responsible for the bioluminescence in Barnegat Bay last October and agrees that the copepods had possibly ingested this algae.

On October twenty-fourth, while anchored in a perfectly calm, dark cove just north of Cedar Creek in the bay, I observed a moving luminescent wave phenomenon, faint but distinct, traveling at about 1.5 m per minute. It described a smooth arc six to eight m in length, which, though it appeared to be on or near the surface, seemed to pass unbroken "under" the boat which draws two-and-a-half feet. The "wave" itself was fifteen or twenty cm wide, smooth and defined on its leading edge and grew faint by degrees on its trailing edge. It is my feeling that it represented a mass of rapid movement of copepods, perhaps agitated by an underwater shock wave, the feeding of larger organisms, or perhaps spontaneous flailing against the water and each other, so they luminesced, producing the observed phenomenon.

The bloom, and these observations, coincided at the end of a very long period of dry, unseasonably warm weather. The corrected bay water temperature was 60.5 F . . .

. . . Many observations of luminescence were made at intervals during the warmer months of 1962 and 1963. Counts were made on the ocean beach and of free-swimming organisms in the bay. In the absence of accurate light-measuring equipment, a comparator (visual comparison chart of known density) was used to determine the intensity of bioluminescence. Readings were taken under as nearly standard circumstances as possible. Values were ultimately expressed as a percentage of the maximum reading (October 1963 bloom).

With whatever confidence two years of observation can give, it can be said that bioluminescence in the ocean appears in late March or early April and is distributed in two general groups of higher readings with a lull, or lulls, about midsummer. It terminates in November, apparently as a consequence of water temperatures below 45° F. . . .

"A Survey of Fishes Along the Beaches of the Hudson-Raritan Estuary," F. Steimle and E. Geer, Jr., *Underwater Naturalist,* Vol. 8, No. 3

The Hudson-Raritan estuary is a wedge-shaped body of water bordered by Brooklyn and Staten Island, New York to the north and the New Jersey coast to the south. Into this estuary flow the Hudson, Raritan, Hackensack, Passaic (around Staten Island), and Shrewsbury Rivers. This estuary is adjacent to one of the largest population concentrations in the world, the New York City metropolis, which in the past looked to it as an important source of seafood, including oysters and lobsters, as well as for recreation. The bordering marshes and shallows were important feeding, spawning, and nursery grounds for many species of fish. In this century this once productive and enjoyable body of water has been severely degraded by millions of gallons of partly or entirely untreated sewage and other pollutants, and by filling in of the marshes.

This degraded state has caused some short-sighted people to think that the estuary is almost dead, in a practical sense, and projects like filling in part of it as a jetport, creating islands in it from garbage or dredging it out for supertankers have been suggested.

In 1973, some New Jersey members of the Littoral Society decided to create a task force to, among other projects, investigate how much fish life was still in the estuary. We thought this project worthwhile, especially in light of the newly created Gateway National Recreation Area, most of which borders the estuary. We chose to make use of the many people who had expressed interest in doing something more than acknowledge the fact that the estuary was in bad shape. With these amateur naturalists we designed a survey of census, using the simple beach seine, of the small fish which occur near the shore, to provide some idea about the abundance of bait fish and juvenile or young game and food fish in the estuary.

Our survey plan was simple: we divided the estuary into six arbitrary sections and asked our volunteers to choose a beach

Sections Caught spans columns A–G*. _Months Caught_ spans columns Apr–Oct.

Species	Total Caught	Total hauls Coll.	Apr	May	Jun	Jul	Aug	Sept.	Oct	A	B	C	D	E	F	G*
Bay Anchovy	186	6		X	X	X			X	X	X		X			X
American eel	7	4											X			
Atlantic needlefish	2	2											X			X
Mummichog	144	13	X	X	X	X	X	X	X	X		X	X		X	
Striped killifish	57	4				X	X	X		X			X		X	
N. pipefish	62	11		X	X	X	X	X	X	X	X	X	X		X	
Bluefish	62	8				X(SA)	X(SA)	X		X	X		X		X	
Spot	17	4				X(SA)	X	X				X	X	X		
N. kingfish	35	9		X		X	X	X		X		X	X	X	X	
Silversides	3047	23		X	X	X	X	X		X	X	X	X		X	
Tomcod	2	2		X		X			X				X			
Menhaden	2	1						X(J)					X			
Alewife	1	1		X(SA)						X	X	X	X	X	X	X
Winter flounder	30	12	X		X	X	X	X	X	X	X	X	X		X	
Sand lance	14	2		X		X			X			X	X		X	
Mullet	37	3					X	X	X	X					X	
Tautog	4	2				X(SA)	X(SA)	X(SA)		X	B					
Jack	2	2				X	X(SA)	X(SA)				X				X
Windowpane	1	1	X													
3-spined stickleback	1	1	X												X	
Majorra	1	1								X					X	
Jack crevalle	1	1			X(J)			X(J)	X(J)	X						
Squirrel hake	2	2									X					
Pompano	1	1						X(J)			X					
Pollock	1	1			X(SA)										X	
Toadfish	2	1							X(SA)							

(J) Juvenile (SA) Sub Adult *Conashonk Point

List of species collected, total numbers of each species caught, the number of times (hauls) the species was collected, and the distribution of the species by month and by section.

within the estuary that was convenient to them which also distributed the seining so that there was at least one pair of seiners in each section. A special area was also chosen near a proposed power plant site at Conaskonk Point in New Jersey. Eight seining sites were thus established from Coney Island to the bay side of Sandy Hook.

We seined twice a month from May through October, using an inexpensive 40-by-4 foot, $\frac{3}{16}$-inch mesh seine. We hauled the seine about 100 feet parallel along the beach, then dragged it up on the beach where we identified and counted the catch. This was done as quickly as possible so the catch could be returned to the water, for the most part, unharmed. We held seminars throughout the season to aid seiners in identifying the many fish they collected.

The first census produced excellent results. Twenty-seven species of fish were collected, including young of important food or game fish like bluefish, winter flounder, tautog, pollock, spot, hake, and eels. Of equal importance were the numbers of "bait fish," food of many adult food and game fish, that were also collected. These bait fish included bay anchovies, killifish, silversides, menhaden, alewives, mullet, and sand lances.

Perhaps the most important finding of this initial census, which will be continued, is that there are still fish using the estuary for nursery grounds and for feeding and there is a good chance, with the cleaning up of these waters with new and better treatment plants, these fish may increase in the estuary, providing more seafood and recreation for the metropolitan area. . . .

BIOCHEMICAL OXYGEN DEMAND AS A MEASURE OF ENTRAINMENT LOSS AT A NUCLEAR POWER STATION, C. O'Neill, D. Doyle, O. Donovan, and E. Kearns, *Underwater Naturalist,* Vol. 10, No. 3

Given that if a steam-electric generating facility is located on an estuary, its cooling water will be heavily populated by a wide range of organisms including zooplankton, phytoplankton, larval and adult fishes and crabs, and Ctenophores. Population densities will depend upon a number of different factors, the most significant of which is season of the year. Total organism densities, for example, will be much higher during the warmer months of the year than in winter.

Organism damage at power plants employing once-through cooling modes can occur in a number of different ways, including impingement on intake screens and entrainment through the condensers. While conducting work on fish distributions in Barnegat Bay in the vicinity of the Oyster Creek nuclear facility, we were impressed with the large biomass of organisms in the intake canal (the South Branch of Forked River). Given the considerable flow of water through the plant, 2,000 cfs (cubic feet per second) in summer, and the very high water velocities in the canal associated with this, it was apparent that non- or weakly-swimming organisms would be unable to avoid the cooling system of the plant. Organisms in this category would include plankton, larval and small fishes and crustaceans, and ctenophores (comb-jellies). Comb-jellies were noted in very large numbers being carried up the intake canal toward the intake structure. Sampling in the intake canal in summer was rendered impractical by seine because of the high water velocities and numbers of comb-jellies.

Since a considerable biomass was obviously being entrained at the plant, it was decided to attempt to gain some quantitative measure of this. Direct sampling at the intake and discharge was not practical due to plant security restrictions and so we reasoned that the five-day BOD (biochemical oxygen demand) could be used as an indirect measure of entrainment losses. The rationale behind this is simply that dead and damaged organisms and pieces of organisms will exert an oxygen demand in the discharge water. BODs in the discharge water, then, could be compared with intake BODs for a rough measure of entrainment damage.

The study cited here was done in July of 1976 and consisted of six samples, on six sampling dates, taken from the intake and discharge canals. Samples were taken from the Route 9 crossings of the canals and incubated for five days at 20° C. The table shows intake and discharge BODs for these sampling dates. Of interest is the fact that a significant difference does exist between intake and discharge, averaging 1.66 mg/1 of BOD.

COMPARATIVE BIOCHEMICAL OXYGEN DEMAND

Date	Intake	Discharge	Difference
1976	mg/1	mg/1	mg/1
July 12	1.80	3.80	2.00
July 16	2.35	3.65	1.50
July 21	4.80	6.30	1.50
July 23	3.50	5.10	1.60
July 28	2.25	4.30	2.05
July 29	2.30	3.60	1.30

Average difference 1.66

The significance of this number is not only as a measure of entrainment damage but also what it implies with respect to the organic loading of the near bay. For example, while the BOD difference of 1.66 mg/1 may not seem very large in itself, it should be kept in mind that the figure is presented as a concentration, not a BOD loading. It is useful to convert mg/1 to an organic loading of lb./day, a commonly used engineering unit. This, of course, takes into account the very large daily discharge from the plant.

Performing this conversion, we calculate that the organic loading of the near bay due to Oyster Creek effluent was roughly 17,000 pounds of oxygen demand on average over the period of the study. For comparison's sake, a large primary sewage treatment plant with capacity of 25 mgd (million gallons per day) with a discharge BOD of 100 mg/1, would cause a loading of roughly 21,000 pounds per day. It is worthy of note that a treatment plant of this type and capacity would not be allowed to discharge into Barnegat Bay. . . .

It should also be mentioned here that BOD differences in winter are proving to be considerably less than in the summer study cited here. This might be what one would expect due to decreased biomass in winter. Summertime, however, is the time of most concern due to higher rates of BOD in the warmer bay waters. This might lead to critically low dissolved oxygen levels in receiving water. Occasionally, rather strong odors of hydrogen sulfide at the mouth of Oyster Creek in summer suggest that this might be the case. . . .

"LITTORAL SAND SIZE VARIATIONS ON LONG ISLAND BEACHES," R. Moroff and J. Kane, *Underwater Naturalist*, Vol. 10, No. 3

A suitable and useful topic for research along marine coastal areas is the measurement of littoral (tidal zone) particle size variations. Particle sizes are affected by three factors: the source material being eroded, the sedimentary characteristics of the depositional forces (waves, currents, and tides), and the location of inlets, jetties, and dredging outfalls. We selected for analysis the South Shore of Long Island, New York because of its accessibility and interesting geologic history. All samples were collected on October 5 and 6, 1974, from the mid-tide zone at thirty sites along the entire length of Long Island's beaches.

The beaches extend 193 km from Montauk Point west to Coney Island and are composed of sands primarily derived by wave undercutting of both glacial moraine cliffs and ancient, wind-formed, sand dune cliffs along the easternmost 50 km of the South Shore. The littoral drift carries sand westward. This sand eventually ends up in the New York Bight, where it is periodically flushed out across the continental shelf by water movements through the upper Hudson Submarine Canyon. Pebbles and larger size particles sit on the beaches below the glacial cliffs until wave action grinds them up into smaller transportable sizes, while silt and clay particles are carried away from littoral coastal areas by moving waters where they are deposited in quiet offshore regions beyond the sublittoral.

Six major inlets (Shinnecock, Moriches, Fire Island, Jones, East Rockaway, and Rockaway) separate segments of the 143 km of barriers. Jetties on the eastern sides of the inlets capture sands from the westward-moving littoral currents that build up the beaches there. The underloaded currents then sweep past the inlets where they cause severe beach erosion on the western (downcurrent) sides. Dredging from the bays and inlets are from time to time dumped there to compensate for the erosion.

Here is how we sampled. After a week of calm, clear weather, samples were collected from the littoral surf zone between waves, when all the sand grains were at rest. All samples were processed according to established procedures. After being thoroughly washed and oven-dried, each sample was split with a sample splitter (Fisher Scientific Co.), until a 100 to 150 gram portion remained. Sieving was done with a U.S. Standard Sieve Series, ASTM specifications (Fisher) and a Ro-Tap Testing Sieve Shaker (W. S. Tyler Co.). Sieve mesh sizes used were 10, 18, 35, 60, 120, 230, and pan. The fractions of each sample were then weighed, and the percentages by weight of each fraction was determined.

The midpoint diameters (in mm) for each sieve size were converted into a standard unit (phi) and then plotted on a graph against the cumulative weight percentages. After drawing a smooth curve through the points, phi values at the 16th, 50th, and 84th percentiles were averaged and converted back into millimeters.

From our studies of the samples, we gathered the following results:

1) Littoral sand particles just below the eroding cliffs of the glacial and dune areas (sites 1–9) were significantly larger (0.48 mm average) than littoral particles along the barriers (0.35 mm average). This illustrates the effects of sorting and erosional attrition on the sand particles as they are being transported westward by littoral currents. Sorting is considered more important because of the minimal change in particle shape that was observed.

2) The Dune Cliff area (sites 5–9) had the largest average littoral particle size (0.52 mm average) and the Coney Island area (sites 29, 30) had the smallest (0.23 mm average). The former may be due to stronger currents along the Dune Cliff area than along the Glacial Cliff area or to previous sorting out of finer particles by the Pleistocene winds that formed the dunes, while the latter reflects the normal sorting effects of currents that have traveled farthest from the source regions.

3) Littoral particle sizes do not decrease uniformly westward along the barriers. Inlets and jetties cause deposition of larger-than-normal particles on the up current (eastern) side, and erosion of normal sized particles on the down current (western) sides. In addition, replenishment of barrier beach sands over the years using small-sized particles dredged from bays and inlets has

provided an extra source of sand for the barrier littoral than would otherwise be available.

4) The sharpest decreases in particle sizes occurred just west of the major inlets. An average decrease of 28% was noted from

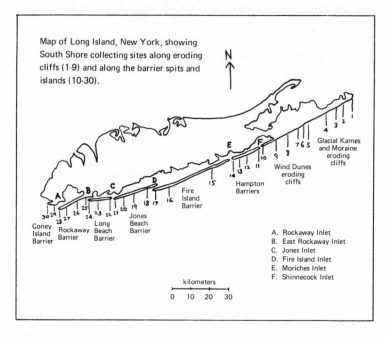

Map of Long Island, New York, showing South Shore collecting sites along eroding cliffs (1-9) and along the barrier spits and islands (10-30).

Littoral Area	Site	Folk (mm) Average	% of Dune Cliff Average
1) Glacial Cliffs	(1–4)	.44	85%
2) Dune Cliffs	(5–9)	.52	100%
3) Hampton Barriers	(10–14)	.45	87%
4) Fire Island Barrier	(15–17)	.37	71%
5) Jones Beach Barrier	(18–21)	.43	83%
6) Long Beach Barrier	(22–24)	.30	58%
7) Rockaway Barrier	(25–28)	.26	50%
8) Coney Island Barrier	(29–30)	.23	44%

Littoral sand size averages (Folk mm means) for eight major sections of Long Island's south shore.

the eastern to the western side of five inlets: Shinnecock, Fire Island, Jones, East Rockaway, and Rockaway. Small-sized bay dredgings dumped on the west sides of inlets are responsible for this phenomenon. No sample was taken close enough to Moriches Inlet to determine any relationship. A slight decrease in particle size west of inlets was noted by Taney (N. E. Taney, "Littoral Materials of the South Shore of Long Island, N.Y." Corps of Engineers' Tech. Memo 129, 1961.

5) The largest sized particles for a single site (0.66 mm average) were at site 10 just east of Shinnecock Inlet. This is due to site 10 being on the up current side of a large inlet jetty, and adjacent to and down current from the Dune Cliff area. Particle sizes decreased generally but irregularly both east and west of site 10, which is located 58 km west of Montauk Point. Taney (referred to above), analyzing 250 samples, collected over a nineteen-year period (1936–1955), found particle sizes generally decreased from Montauk Point westward, but with large variations in the Glacial Cliff section. This supports the possibility that, while the westerly decrease from site 10 is due to normal sorting, the easterly decrease may be due to occasionally variable currents. . . .

15

BROADENING YOUR HORIZONS

A Faustian consequence of a thirst for deeper understanding is an unquenchable desire for more. How you go about slaking that thirst depends on where you start when you begin your search. More formal education, reading more extensively and more intently, locating a mentor to guide you over rough spots, finding sources of materials and specimens, and delving into the scientific literature are all pathways to broader horizons.

You may decide your interests lie more in conservation or in helping someone else uncover new knowledge. Either will bring you into contact with others of similar persuasion and their experiences may help widen your own perspective.

ACADEMIC TRAINING

Your local university or college may offer useful night courses in biology and ecology. Normally, you must take academic coursework in a certain sequence, starting with prerequisite courses that lay the framework for the more specific courses to follow.

If you choose this path, be prepared to work hard. Introductory courses are full of many new concepts whose applications are not immediately obvious. You cannot pick and choose what you intend to learn. You must absorb the bulk of it without discrimination, for an obscure point missed now may be critical to understanding a concept presented in a later course. You cannot afford to meet new ideas later on with only a hazy notion of the bedrock on which they rest.

If you are retired, you may be in for a pleasant surprise. Many state universities will offer you a place in their classrooms for a fraction of the fees paid by the typical university student.

FIELD STATIONS

A number of institutions, either singly or collectively, maintain field stations that offer short (one to six weeks) courses that invariably involve field work. Some of these are survey courses well within the grasp of anyone with a sound, general education. Normally room and board are included, and the lifestyle for its duration is a refreshing mix of hard work, long hours, and fun.

Natural history and conservation organizations occasionally run field trips that have a marine theme. At this writing, the American Littoral Society conducts a number of marine natural history trips. One such, to Bermuda, operates from the Bermuda Biological Station for Research, which has the added advantage of opportunities to browse in a marine library and become familiar with the type of work that goes on at a research field station.

One of the advantages of age are courses offered through Elderhostel. These are one week long and inexpensive. Aside from low cost, they are often located at first-rate field stations where you can use your free time to assimilate what services, exhibits, and expertise the institution has to offer.

READING

Textbooks and popular literature tend to be filled with generalities which suffice for a time, but are not much help when you want to delve more into the habits of a specific animal, the associations in a particular habitat, or the goings-on in a specific geographic locale.

Getting to the scientific literature is slow going if you are not connected with a well-stocked marine science library or a departmental university library.

Nevertheless, it's not impossible. You can track down specific information by starting with a review article (say, in *Scientific American*) close to your interests. Go to the references given in that article which usually are scientific papers, then look into the references in those papers.

A helpful local librarian can save you time and effort if you enlist that person in your search. The librarian can check the county and state system for the journals you seek, and if that doesn't pan out, can help you check with a local university or an out-of-state library. You rarely can take a journal out of a library, but most have a copying service for a modest fee.

A source of information on specific animals, habitats, and conservation problems is the Fish and Wildlife Service. They publish a Species Profile Series and a Community Profile Series that covers a specific kind of locale thoroughly. For a broader coverage of marine topics, try the Sea Grant publications and search service. If you have a particular subject in mind they will conduct a search of the Sea Grant publications which covers participating institutions. They will either get you a reprint or tell you where to send for it.

As you come across articles with bibliographies, make a note of any topical references that might pique your curiosity. At first, you might simply list them in your journal. If they begin to accumulate, a card or computer file might be a better bet, making it easier to lump like references into useful categories.

MATERIALS

Both apparatus and specimens are available from well-known supply houses. It makes no sense to spend time and effort seeking out a specific specimen if you can buy it, live or preserved, from a biological supply house.

MENTORS

Rarely will your exact interests coincide with those of a trained professional, but if they do, you may be able to create a quid pro quo arrangement. The professional may need extra hands to help with field work or boat time, or a skill you possess which will give you an opportunity to work and meet others who share your interests.

You may be able to join a team for a week or more working on a specific project in the field. Contact Earthwatch for expeditions involving marine topics.

CONSERVATION

A number of environmental groups are now running citizen monitoring programs. This may entail training followed by periodic field work and analysis.

Environmental groups need dedicated people to help with a wide variety of tasks, from participation at events such as beach clean-ups and demonstrations for clean water, to attending and commenting at government hearings and meetings.

Taking an active role in marine conservation issues must be prefaced by doing your homework. You should know the ecosystem you plan to defend, both through reading and field work. You must also understand both the local and state positions on the issue and have a good grasp of the related laws.

We have more than sufficient coastal pollution problems that need attention. For a recapitulation of the major ones, the appropriate laws, and what you can do, see Bulloch's *The Wasted Ocean*.

A PARTING THOUGHT

If the sea evokes a deep-seated passion in you, you have the makings of a life-long avocation, or, if you choose and have the resolve, a career.

Whether it is to be a career or avocation, do not underestimate your own capacity to learn what is worth knowing, to glimpse what is worth seeing, and to reflect on what is worth contemplating. You will never know it all, see it all, or understand it all, but neither will any other human. That is the essence of its attraction.

APPENDIX A

MEASURING DISSOLVED OXYGEN IN SEAWATER BY WINKLER (IODOMETRIC) TITRATION

Iodometry is the basis of the most precise and reliable method for measuring DO. Divalent manganese and strong alkali are added to an enclosed sample of water. The DO in the sample oxidizes an equivalent amount of divalent manganese hydroxide dispersion to a higher valence state. Upon acidifying the sample in the presence of iodide ion, the oxidized manganese reverts to the divalent state and iodine is released equivalent to the original DO content of the sample. The iodine is then titrated with a standard solution of thiosulfate. The reaction steps are outlined on page 117.

The end point of the titration can be detected visually with a starch indicator or electrometrically using a potentiometric technique. A precision of fifty micrograms per liter can be achieved with the visual end point and ± 5 micrograms per liter using an electrometric method. To reduce analysis time, iodine can be measured directly by absorption spectrophotometry.

The analysis is subject to interference by nitrite, iron, and suspended solids. Analysis modifications can eliminate these interferences (see Taras, et. al., 1971, "Standard Methods for the Examination of Water and Wastewater" American Public Health Association, Washington, D.C.). Nitrite is often present in waters enriched by sewage. Its interference can be negated by the addition of sodium azide; that is the method presented here.

SAMPLE COLLECTION:

Collect the sample in a standard 300 ml narrow-mouth, glass-stoppered BOD bottle without agitation or prolonged contact with air.

REAGENTS NEEDED

Manganese sulfate solution—dissolve 480 g of $MnSO_4 \cdot 4H_2O$ in distilled water, filter, and dilute to one liter. The solution should not give a color with starch when added to an acidified solution of potassium iodide.

Alkali-Iodide-Azide solution—dissolve 500 g of sodium hydroxide and 150 g of potassium iodide in distilled water (or stoichiometric equivalents of KOH or NaI) and dilute to one liter. Dissolve 10 g of sodium azide in 40 ml of distilled water and add to the above solution. This solution should not give a color with starch when diluted and acidified.

Sulfuric acid, concentrated—36N

Starch solution—suspend 5 g of soluble starch in about 100 ml of cold water and add to 800 ml of boiling water while stirring. Dilute to one liter and again bring to a boil. Let it cool and settle overnight. Bottle the clear supernate. Add 1 g of salicylic acid as a preservative.

Standard sodium thiosulfate (0.025N)—dissolve 6.205 g $Na_2S_2O_3 \bullet 5H_2O$ in freshly boiled and cooled distilled water. Add 0.4 g NaOH as a preservative and dilute to one liter.

Standardize the thiosulfate solution with potassium dichromate.

Dissolve 1.226 g of analytical grade $K_2Cr_2O_7$ (previously dried at 150° C for two hours) in distilled water and dilute to exactly one liter. This solution is 0.0250N.

To an Erlenmeyer flask containing 100 ml of water, add 2 g potassium iodide and 1 ml of concentrated sulfuric acid. Then add exactly 20.00 ml of 0.0250N sodium dichromate solution. Let stand in the dark for five minutes, dilute to 400 ml, then titrate with 0.025N sodium thiosulfate solution. Add starch indicator toward the end of the titration (about 19 ml).

Since it is convenient to adjust the thiosulfate solution to exactly 0.0250N, a 0.1N thiosulfate stock solution (or water) can be used to adjust it until exactly 20.00 ml is required to reach the endpoint with the dichromate solution.

DO DETERMINATION

To the sample (in a 250–300 ml full, glass-stoppered BOD bottle), add 2 ml of manganese sulfate solution, then 2 ml of alkali-iodide-azide solution. Introduce each liquid below the surface and restopper the bottle without entrapping air and mix by inverting about fifteen times. Let settle, reshake, then let resettle for at least two minutes.

Remove the stopper, add 2 ml of concentrated sulfuric acid, restopper, and mix until the floc has dissolved and the iodine color is evenly distributed. Withdraw 203 ml of sample and titrate with 0.0250N sodium thiosulfate until the color of the solution retains just a hint of yellow.

Add 1 to 2 ml of starch solution and continue the titration until the blue color just disappears. Ignore any subsequent recoloration on standing.

CALCULATIONS

One ml of 0.0250N sodium thiosulfate titrant is equal to 0.200 mg of DO, therefore 1 ml of 0.0250N sodium thiosulfate titrant used is equivalent to 1 mg/1. DO when titrating a 200 ml sample. (The 203 ml aliquot takes into account the increase in volume by the added reactants.)

APPENDIX B
MEASURING SALINITY BY CHLORIDE TITRATION

APPARATUS NEEDED
25 ml burette
10 ml volumetric pipettes
1 ml volumetric pipette
1 l. volumetric flask
beakers, reagent bottles, etc.

REAGENTS NEEDED
Potassium chromate solution: Dissolve 5 g of potassium chromate (K_2CrO_4) in one liter of distilled water.
Silver nitrate solution: Weigh out exactly 2.400 g of silver nitrate ($AgNO_3$) and dissolve in one liter of distilled water. Store solution in the dark.

PROCEDURE
Measure exactly 10.0 ml of seawater into a beaker via a volumetric pipette. Add exactly 10.0 ml of distilled water via volumetric pipette and mix thoroughly.

Transfer exactly 1.00 ml of the accurately diluted seawater to a beaker. Prepare three such samples.

Add 10 ml of potassium chromate solution to each beaker.

Titrate each sample with the silver nitrate solution until the yellow color of the chromate just permanently turns to a faint coffee or reddish-brown tint. Record the number of mls (estimate to the nearest one-hundredth of a ml) required for each of three samples. Average the results.

The average titration in mls is equal to chlorinity in parts per thousand. To calculate salinity:

$$\text{Salinity (ppt)} = 0.03 + 1.805 \times \text{chlorinity (ppt)}$$

SELECTED REFERENCES

CHAPTER 1

Choose a textbook on statistics by reading the introductory chapters, which will cover frequency distributions, the mean and standard deviation, and normal distribution. If you grasp those concepts, plunge on into tests of significance and the rest of the book. If the author does not make the basic points clear to you, try another text.

There are many good introductory texts. A well-known standard is

Snedecor, G. and Cochran, W. 1980. *Statistical methods*. Ames: Iowa State University Press.

If you have a college level background in mathematics and a bent for quantitative thinking, a delightful way to stretch those little gray cells can be found in

Harte, J. 1985. *Consider a spherical cow: a course in environmental problem solving*. Los Altos, California: W. Kaufmann Inc.

CHAPTER 2

For piloting and other aspects of seamanship try

Mahoney, E. 1987. *Chapman piloting, seamanship, and small boat handling*. New York, New York: William Morrow & Sons.

Triangulation methods from shore objects are standard ship's practice (for example, to insure the anchor isn't dragging). That and all the standard methods of ship's navigation can be found in this classic.

Bowditch, N. *American practical navigator*. H.O Pub. 9 (available from Superintendent of Documents, Washington, D.C.).

CHAPTER 3

For an introduction into the mysteries of invertebrate life

Pearse, V.; Pearse, J.; Buchsbaum, M.; and Buchsbaum, R. 1987. *Living invertebrates*. Palo Alto, California: Blackwell Scientific Publications.

Guide books for identifying marine invertebrates are listed here. For other species such as fish, look under the appropriate chapter heading.

This listing is by no means complete nor are all the books listed still in print

Dawson, E. 1956. *How to know the seaweeds*. Dubuque, Iowa: Wm. C. Brown Company.

Gosner, K. 1979. *Field guide to the Atlantic seashore*. Boston: Houghton Mifflin Company.

Kaplan, E. H. 1982. *A field guide to coral reefs*. Boston: Houghton Mifflin Company.

———. 1988. *A field guide to Southeastern and Caribbean seashores*. Boston: Houghton Mifflin Company.

Miner, R. 1950. *Field book of seashore life*. New York: Putnam's and Sons.

Morris, R.; Abbott, D.; and Haderlie, E. 1980. *Intertidal invertebrates of California*. Stanford, California: Stanford University Press.

Ruppert, E. E., and Fox, R. S. 1988. *Seashore animals of the Southeast*. Columbia: University of South Carolina.

Smith, R., and J. Carlton 1975. *Light's manual: Intertidal invertebrates of the Central California Coast*. Berkeley: University of California.

Here are the names of a few booksellers who specialize in books on biology, nature, conservation, and the environment

Cachalot Bookshop
Mystic Marinelife Aquarium
Mystic, CT 06355-1997

Patrica Ledlie Bookseller, Inc.
One Bean Road, P.O. Box 90
Buckfield, ME 04220

CHAPTER 4

For more on collecting and preserving try

Rudloe, J. 1971. *The erotic ocean*. New York: World Publishing.

Getting acquainted with a specific location can be made easier by reading a general description of typical locales nearby as well as delving into identification manuals.

Berrill, M., and Berrill, D. 1981. *A Sierra Club nature guide: the North Atlantic Coast*. San Francisco: Sierra Club Books.

Bulloch, D. K. 1991. *Underwater naturalist*. New York: Lyons and Burford.

Kozloff, E. 1983. *Seashore life of the Northern Pacific*. Seattle: University of Washington Press.

Perry, W. 1985. *A Sierra Club naturalist's guide: the Middle Atlantic Coast*. San Francisco: Sierra Club Books.

Ricketts, E., et. al. 1985. *Between Pacific tides*, 5th ed. Stanford, California: Stanford University Press.

CHAPTER 5

For an overview on the oceans try

Herring, P., and Clarke, M. 1971. *Deep oceans*. New York: Praeger Publishers.

Going whalewatching? Start by learning to identify whales.

Leatherwood S.; Caldwell, D.; and Winn, H. 1978. *Whales, dolphins, and porpoises of the Western North Atlantic*. NOAA Tech. Report NMFS CIRC 396.

Leatherwood, S., et. al. 1982. *Whales, dolphins, and porpoises of the Eastern Pacific and adjacent waters*. NOAA Tech. Report NMFS CIRC 444.

For small-sized oceanographic instruments write

Wildlife Supply Co.

301 Cass Street

Saginaw, MI 48602

CHAPTER 6

More important than knowing one species of fish from another is a general background about fish.

Bulloch, D. 1986. *Marine game fishes of the Middle Atlantic*. Sandy Hook, New Jersey: American Littoral Society.

Bigelow, H., and Schroeder, W. 1952. *Fishes of the Gulf of Maine*. Fishery Bulletin of the Fish and Wildlife Service, Vol. 53. Reprinted by Harvard University Press, Cambridge, MA.

Curtis, B. 1949. *The life story of a fish*. New York: Dover Publications.

Marshall, N. 1966. *The life of fishes*. New York: Universe Books.

For fish identification

Castro, J. 1983. *The sharks of North America*. College Station, Texas: Texas A&M University Press.

Eschmeyer, W. N., Herald, E. S., and Hammann, H. 1983. *Field guide to Pacific fishes*. Boston: Houghton Mifflin Company.

Hoese, H. D., and Moore, R. H. 1977. *Fishes of the Gulf of Mexico*. College Station, Texas: Texas A&M University Press.

Randall, J. 1968. *Caribbean reef fishes*. Neptune, New Jersey: T.H.F. Publications.

Stokes, J. 1980. *Coral reef fishes of the Caribbean*. London: Collins.

For tagging small marine game species contact the following for tags and know-how

American Littoral Society
Sandy Hook, NJ 07732

For billfish and tuna contact

Southeast Fisheries Center
75 Virginia Beach Drive
Miami, FL 33149

or

Southwest Fisheries Center
P.O. Box 271
La Jolla, CA 92027

For sharks, contact

NOAA/NMFS Narragansett Laboratory
South Ferry Road
Narragansett, RI 02882

CHAPTER 7

The classics of behavioral study are

Lorenz, K. 1981. *The foundations of ethology*. New York: Simon and Schuster.

Tinbergen, N. 1969. *The study of instinct*. London: Oxford University Press.

Wilson, E. 1978. *Sociobiology*. Cambridge, Massachusetts: Harvard University Press.

For a book on observing and drawing conclusions that you can easily duplicate for yourself read

Tinbergen, N. 1967. *The herring gull's world*. Garden City, New York: Doubleday.

CHAPTER 8

Books in print on plankton are getting scarce. The first is a classic, the rest concern identification.

Hardy, A. 1965. *The open sea: the world of plankton*. Boston: Houghton Mifflin Company.

Newell, G., and Newell, R. 1965. *Marine plankton*. New York: Hutchinson.

Smith, D. L. 1977. *A guide to marine coastal plankton and marine invertebrate larvae*. Dubuque, Iowa: Kendall/Hunt Publishing.

Wickstead, J. 1965. *An introduction to the study of tropical plankton*. New York: Hutchinson.

CHAPTER 9

The field of microorganism systematics is moving fast these days as new biochemical methods are applied (see C. R. Woese, *Microbiol. Rev.* 51, 221. 1987).

For a description of bacteria's role in ocean processes try

Wood, E. 1967. *Microbiology of oceans and estuaries*. New York: Elsevier Publishing.

CHAPTER 10

There are many out-of print texts on the use of the microscope. Here are several that are still available

Delly, J. G. *Photography through the microscope*. Rochester, New York: Eastman Kodak Company.

Grave, E. 1986. *Discovering the invisible*. Englewood Cliffs, New Jersey: Prentice-Hall. (Now available through Dover Pub.)

Needham, C. A. 1977. *The practical use of the microscope*. Springfield, Illinois: Thomas.

CHAPTER 11

Because specific camera models change so rapidly and there are so many general books on photography, you will do better to browse in the reading section of a relatively large photo store. For underwater photography, try a well-stocked dive shop.

CHAPTER 12

For more on the analysis of seawater try

Parsons, T.; Maita, Y.; and Lalli, C. 1984. *A manual of chemical and biological methods for seawater analysis*. New York: Pergamon Press.

To obtain kits for dissolved oxygen analysis (and other water analyses) contact either company and find out who is their closest distributor.

Hach Corp.
P.O. Box 389
Loveland, CO 80539

or

LaMotte Chemical Products
P.O. Box 329
Chestertown, MD 21620

For a DO meter
Yellow Springs Instrument Co.
Yellow Springs, Ohio 45387

CHAPTER 13

Avoid old references to marine aquariums. Since the advent of plastics and good, artificial seawater, marine aquarium keeping has become considerably easier.

Bower, C. E. 1983. *The basic marine aquarium*. Springfield, Illinois: Thomas Publishing.

Moe, M. A. 1982. *Marine aquarium handbook*. Marathon, Florida: Norns Publishing.

National Research Council 1981. *Marine invertebrates*. Washington, D.C.: National Academy Press.

Spotte, S. 1979. *Seawater aquariums*. New York: John Wiley.

CHAPTER 14

For ideas on field studies that you can do read whatever natural history publications you can and go on as many field trips as you can. If you join the American Littoral Society you will receive its publication, *Underwater Naturalist*. Also visit aquariums for ideas. See: Pacheco, A., and S. Smith. 1989. *Marine parks and aquaria*. New York: Lyons and Burford.

CHAPTER 15

If you have not as yet learned to snorkel, read

Clark, John R. 1986. *Snorkeling: a complete guide to the underwater experience*. Englewood Cliffs, New Jersey: Prentice-Hall.

For a list of field stations offering courses, write

Organization of Biological Field Stations
P.O. Box 351
Eureka, MO 63025
For a list of Elderhostel courses write
Elderhostel
80 Boylston Street, Suite 400
Boston, MA 02116
For new publications from the Fish and Wildlife Service, write
U.S. Fish and Wildlife Service
Publications Unit
18th and C Street, NW
Room 130–ARLSQ
Washington, D.C. 20248
For current publications from the National Sea Grant Program, write
National Sea Grant Depository
Pell Library Building/Bay Campus
University of Rhode Island
Narragansett, RI 02882
and request to be put on the "Sea Grant Abstracts" mailing list.
Two well-known biological supply houses are
Carolina Biological Supply Co.
2700 York Ave.
Burlington, NC 27215
and
Ward's Natural Science Establishment
3000 Ridge Road
P.O. Box 1712
Rochester, NY 14613
For expeditions where you pay your way, help support the leader financially, then work on the leader's project, write
Earthwatch
680 Mount Auburn Street
Watertown, MA 02272

INDEX

Page numbers in italics refer to illustrations.